Middle School 2-2

기말고사 완벽대비

KB087544

# 적중100
## 영어 기출 문제집

중2

지학 | 민찬규

*Best Collection*

# 구성과 특징

교과서의 주요 학습 내용을 중심으로 학습 영역별 특성에 맞춰 단계별로 다양한 학습 기회를 제공하여 단원별 학습능력 평가는 물론 중간 및 기말고사 시험 등에 완벽하게 대비할 수 있도록 내용을 구성

## Words & Expressions

**Step1** Key Words 단원별 핵심 단어 설명 및 풀이
Key Expression 단원별 핵심 숙어 및 관용어 설명
Word Power 반대 또는 비슷한 뜻 단어 배우기
English Dictionary 영어로 배우는 영어 단어

**Step2** 실력평가 단원별 수시평가 대비 주관식, 객관식 문제풀이

**Step3** 서술형 대비 학업성취도 및 수행능력평가 대비 서술형 문제풀이

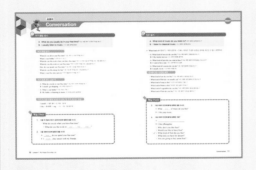

## Conversation

**Step1** 핵심 의사소통 의사소통에 필요한 주요 표현 방법 요약
핵심 Check 기본적인 표현 방법 및 활용능력 확인

**Step2** 대화문 익히기 상황에 따른 대화문 활용 및 연습

**Step3** 기본평가 시험대비 기초 학습 능력 평가

**Step4** 실력평가 단원별 수시평가 대비 주관식, 객관식 문제풀이

**Step5** 서술형 대비 학업성취도 및 수행능력평가 대비 서술형 문제풀이

## Grammar

**Step1** 주요 문법 단원별 주요 문법 사항과 예문을 알기 쉽게 설명
핵심 Check 기본 문법사항에 대한 이해 여부 확인

**Step2** 기본평가 시험대비 기초 학습 능력 평가

**Step3** 실력평가 단원별 수시평가 대비 주관식, 객관식 문제풀이

**Step4** 서술형 대비 학업성취도 및 수행능력평가 대비 서술형 문제풀이

## Reading

**Step1** 구문 분석 단원별로 제시된 문장에 대한 구문별 분석과 내용 설명
확인문제 문장에 대한 기본적인 이해와 인지능력 확인

**Step2** 확인학습A 빈칸 채우기를 통한 문장 완성 능력 확인

**Step3** 확인학습B 제시된 우리말을 영어로 완성하여 작문 능력 키우기

**Step4** 실력평가 단원별 수시평가 대비 주관식, 객관식 문제풀이

**Step5** 서술형 대비 학업성취도 및 수행능력평가 대비 서술형 문제풀이
교과서 구석구석 교과서에 나오는 기타 문장까지 완벽 학습

# Composition

## |영역별 핵심문제|

단어 및 어휘, 대화문, 문법, 독해 등 각 영역별 기출문제의 출제 유형을 분석하여 실전에 대비하고 연습할 수 있도록 문제를 배열

## |서술형 실전 및 창의사고력 문제|

학교 시험에서 점차 늘어나는 서술형 시험에 집중 대비하고 고득점을 취득하는데 만전을 기하기 위한 학습 코너

## |단원별 예상문제|

기출문제를 분석한 후 새로운 시험 출제 경향을 더하여 새롭게 출제될 수 있는 문제를 포함하여 시험에 완벽하게 대비할 수 있도록 준비

## |단원별 모의고사|

영역별, 단계별 학습을 모두 마친 후 실전 연습을 위한 모의고사

## INSIGHT
## on the textbook.................................... 교과서 파헤치기

- **단어Test1~2** 영어 단어 우리말 쓰기와 우리말을 영어 단어로 쓰기
- **대화문Test1~2** 대화문 빈칸 완성 및 전체 대화문 쓰기
- **본문Test1~5** 빈칸 완성, 우리말 쓰기, 문장 배열연습, 영어 작문하기 복습 등 단계별 반복 학습을 통해 교과서 지문에 대한 완벽한 습득
- **구석구석지문Test1~2** 지문 빈칸 완성 및 전문 영어로 쓰기

# Contents

# Magic or Science?

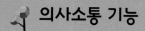 **의사소통 기능**

- 질문하기
  Which sport do you want to learn?
- 희망 · 기대 표현하기
  I can't wait to see the difference.

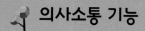 **언어 형식**

- 가주어 It
  **It** is exciting **to watch** a magic show.
- How come ...?
  **How come** the water rose into the glass?

교과서

# Words & Expressions

## Key Words

- **abracadabra** [æbrəkədǽbrə] 명 수리수리마수리 (주문)
- **absorb** [æbsɔ́ːrb] 동 흡수하다
- **balloon** [bəlúːn] 명 풍선
- **behind** [biháind] 전 ~ 뒤에
- **candle** [kǽndl] 명 양초
- **coin** [kɔin] 명 동전
- **compare** [kəmpɛ́ər] 동 비교하다
- **confuse** [kənfjúːz] 동 혼동하게 하다
- **contract** [kəntrǽkt] 동 수축하다
- **difference** [dífərəns] 명 차이, 차이점
- **disappear** [dìsəpíər] 동 사라지다
- **dry** [drai] 형 마른, 비가 오지 않는
- **escape** [iskéip] 동 탈출하다, (액체, 가스가) 새다
- **expand** [ikspǽnd] 동 팽창하다
- **experiment** [ikspérəmənt] 명 실험
- **fill** [fil] 동 채우다
- **flame** [fleim] 명 불꽃
- **flavor** [fléivər] 명 맛
- **float** [flout] 동 뜨다
- **freezer** [fríːzər] 명 냉동고
- **hold** [hould] 동 잡다, 쥐다

- **instead** [instéd] 부 대신에
- **lightning** [láitniŋ] 명 번개
- **magic** [mǽdʒik] 명 마술, 마법
- **material** [mətíəriəl] 명 재료, 물질
- **mix** [miks] 동 섞다
- **move** [muːv] 동 움직이다
- **necessary** [nésəsèri] 형 필요한
- **ocean** [óuʃən] 명 대양, 바다
- **practice** [prǽktis] 명 연습
- **prepare** [pripɛ́ər] 동 준비하다
- **pressure** [préʃər] 명 압력
- **push** [puʃ] 동 밀다
- **rise** [raiz] 동 오르다, 올라가다
- **rose** [rouz] 명 장미
- **safe** [seif] 형 안전한
- **secret** [síːkrit] 명 비밀
- **sink** [siŋk] 동 가라앉다
- **sunburn** [sʌ́nbərn] 명 볕에 탐
- **sunscreen** [sʌ́nskrìːn] 명 자외선 차단제
- **trick** [trik] 명 마술, 속임수
- **weigh** [wei] 동 무게를 재다

## Key Expressions

- **a glass of** 한 잔의
- **burn out** 타 버리다
- **cool down** 차가워지다
- **dry season** 건기
- **for a long time** 오랫동안
- **give it a try** 시도해 보다

- **pick out** 골라내다
- **see through** 속을 들여다 보다
- **sign up for** ~을 신청하다
- **some day** 언젠가, 머지않아
- **stick to** ~을 (바꾸지 않고) 고수하다
- **turn A into B** A가 B로 변하다

## Word Power

※ 서로 반대되는 뜻을 가진 어휘

- **contract** 수축하다 ↔ **expand** 팽창하다
- **dry** 건조한 ↔ **wet** 젖은
- **behind** ~ 뒤에 ↔ **in front of** ~ 앞에
- **necessary** 필요한 ↔ **unnecessary** 불필요한
- **safe** 안전한 ↔ **dangerous** 위험한
- **sink** 가라앉다 ↔ **float** 뜨다

- **fill** 채우다 ↔ **empty** 비우다
- **mix** 섞다 ↔ **separate** 분리하다
- **appear** 나타나다 ↔ **disappear** 사라지다
- **rise** 올라가다 ↔ **drop** 떨어지다
- **careful** 주의 깊은 ↔ **careless** 부주의한
- **absorb** 흡수하다 ↔ **release** 방출하다

## English Dictionary

- **absorb** 흡수하다
  → to take in something in a natural or gradual way
  자연스럽거나 점차적인 방식으로 무언가를 받아들이다

- **confuse** 혼동하다
  → to mistake one person or thing for another
  누군가 또는 어떤 것을 다른 것으로 잘못 알다

- **contract** 수축하다
  → to become smaller
  더 작아지다

- **expand** 팽창하다
  → to increase in size, range, or amount
  크기, 범위, 또는 양에서 증가하다

- **float** 뜨다
  → to rest on top of a liquid or in the air
  액체 맨 윗부분에 또는 공기 중에 있다

- **freezer** 냉동고
  → a device or room for freezing food or keeping it frozen
  음식을 얼리거나 언 채로 유지되도록 하기 위한 장치 또는 공간

- **magic** 마술의
  → having the power to make impossible things happen
  불가능한 일들이 일어나게 만드는 힘을 가진

- **material** 물질, 재료
  → a substance that things can be made from
  무언가가 그로부터 만들 수 있는 재료

- **mix** 섞다
  → to combine two or more substances so that they become a single substance
  두 개 이상의 물질을 결합하여 하나의 물질이 되게 하다

- **practice** 연습
  → the activity of doing something again and again in order to become better at it
  더 잘하기 위해 무언가를 계속해서 하는 활동

- **secret** 비밀
  → a piece of information that is kept hidden from other people 다른 사람들에게 숨겨진 정보

- **sink** 가라앉다
  → to go down below the surface of water
  물의 표면 아래로 내려가다

- **trick** 속임수, 마술
  → something done to surprise or confuse someone
  누군가를 놀라게 하거나 혼란시키기 위해 행해지는 것

- **weigh** 무게를 재다
  → to find how heavy someone or something is
  누군가 또는 무언가가 얼마나 무거운지 알아내다

**01** 다음 짝지어진 단어의 관계가 같도록 빈칸에 알맞은 말을 쓰시오.

> increase : decrease = appear : _____

**02** 다음 영영풀이가 가리키는 것을 고르시오.

> to increase in size, range, or amount

① expand        ② sink
③ float          ④ weigh
⑤ hold

중요

**03** 다음 중 밑줄 친 부분의 뜻풀이가 바르지 <u>않은</u> 것은?

① The material doesn't <u>absorb</u> the water. 흡수하다
② Which things will Ms. Jeong <u>weigh</u> for the test? 무게를 재다
③ I want to learn how to hold a <u>flame</u> without burning my hands. 불꽃
④ I always <u>confuse</u> your bag and mine. 비교하다
⑤ Can you tell me the <u>secret</u> of success? 비밀

**04** 다음 문장에 공통으로 들어갈 말을 고르시오.

> • It is _____ to prepare something for a dry season.
> • This machine is _____ for treating disease.
> • Exercise is _____ to keep your health.

① safe           ② necessary
③ confusing      ④ amazing
⑤ dry

중요

**05** 다음 주어진 문장의 밑줄 친 rose와 같은 의미로 쓰인 것은?

> The sales <u>rose</u> by 20 percent last week.

① The cloud of smoke <u>rose</u> suddenly.
② She drew a <u>rose</u> on her note.
③ Some flowers, like <u>roses</u>, need special care.
④ The prince was looking for a <u>rose</u>.
⑤ When I smelled the <u>rose</u>, I felt so happy.

**06** 다음 우리말에 맞게 빈칸에 알맞은 말을 쓰시오.

(1) 우리는 경비원들을 속이고 지나가기 위해 속임수를 생각해 내어야 했다.
   ➡ We had to think of _____ to get past the guards.
(2) 나는 특별한 물질을 컵 하나에 넣어 두었다.
   ➡ I put a special _____ into one of the cups.
(3) 우리 아빠는 나를 위해 매일 아침을 준비하신다.
   ➡ My father always _____ breakfast for me every day.
(4) 당신은 속을 들여다볼 수 없는 컵을 사용하는 것이 필요하다.
   ➡ It's _____ to use cups that you can't see through.
(5) 공기는 더 높은 압력을 생성한다.
   ➡ Air creates higher _____.
(6) 회사의 확장 계획에 대해 어떻게 생각하세요?
   ➡ What do you think of the company's plans to _____?

**01** 다음 짝지어진 단어의 관계가 같도록 빈칸에 알맞은 말을 쓰시오.

> contract : expand = sink : _____

**02** 다음 문장의 빈칸에 들어갈 말을 〈보기〉에서 골라 쓰시오.

> ┤ 보기 ├
>
> stick to / cooled down / see through /
> turn ~ into / burned out

(1) I can't _____ _____ the window.
(2) The magician can _____ rain _____ snow.
(3) After an hour, the candle _____ _____.
(4) The weather has _____ _____ a little.
(5) I _____ _____ what I think I am good at.

**03** 다음 우리말을 주어진 단어를 이용하여 영작하시오.

(1) 우리는 물고기 대신에 손가락을 사용할 수 있다.
  ➡ We can use a finger _____ of a fish.
(2) 달걀이 물에 뜰 때, 그것들은 신선하지 않다.
  ➡ When eggs _____ in water, they're not fresh.
(3) 마술 공연을 보는 것은 흥미롭다.
  ➡ It's exciting to watch a _____ show.
(4) 그것이 물을 유리컵 속으로 밀었다.
  ➡ It _____ the water into the glass.

**04** 다음 우리말과 일치하도록 주어진 어구를 모두 배열하여 영작하시오.

(1) 네가 싫어하는 채소들을 골라내는 것은 좋지 않다.
  (that / good / to / it / don't / is / pick out / not / you / like / vegetables)
  ➡ _____

(2) 내가 시도해 볼게.
  (it / I'll / a / give / try)
  ➡ _____

(3) 졸리면, 차가운 물 한 잔을 마셔라.
  (drink / if / sleepy / are / you / water / cold / a glass / of)
  ➡ _____

(4) 나는 배드민턴 수업을 신청했다.
  (the / class / badminton / signed / for / up / I)
  ➡ _____

**05** 다음 문장의 빈칸에 들어갈 말을 〈보기〉에서 골라 쓰시오.

> ┤ 보기 ├
>
> hold / coin / sunburn / expands /
> escape / contract

(1) It is necessary to wear sunscreen to prevent _____.
(2) _____ the bottle in your hands for a while.
(3) As the air gets warm, it _____.
(4) You can see how a _____ dances in a bottle.
(5) The expanding air tries to _____ from the bottle.
(6) When you bend your arms, your muscles _____.

교과서

# Conversation

① 질문하기

**Which sport do you want to learn?** 너는 어느 운동을 배우고 싶니?

■ 'Which …?'는 '어느[어떤] …?'라는 뜻으로, 어떤 것을 선택하고자 하는지 묻는 표현이다. Which 뒤에는 sport, flavor, activity 등의 표현이 온다.

### 질문하기

- Which sport do you like? Badminton or soccer? 너는 어느 운동을 좋아하니? 배드민턴 또는 축구?
- What's your favorite color? 가장 좋아하는 색이 무엇이니?

### 선호 말하기

- I like soccer most[best]. 나는 축구를 가장 좋아한다.
- I love playing basketball. 나는 농구하기를 매우 좋아한다.
- I'm fond of ~. 나는 ~을 좋아한다.
- My favorite sport is dodge ball. 내가 가장 좋아하는 운동은 피구이다.
- I enjoy playing baseball (very much). 나는 야구하기를 (매우) 즐긴다.

### 핵심 Check

**1.** 다음 우리말과 일치하도록 빈칸에 알맞은 말을 쓰시오.

(1) **A:** _____ _____ do you want to visit the most? (너는 어느 나라를 가장 방문하고 싶니?)

   **B:** I want to visit Indonesia. (나는 인도네시아를 방문하고 싶어.)

(2) **A:** _____ _____ does Sejun want to play? (세준이는 어느 운동을 하고 싶어 하니?)

   **B:** He wants to play basketball. (그는 농구를 하고 싶어 해.)

(3) **A:** _____ _____ _____ _____, a straw or a potato?

   (짚과 감자 중 어느 것이 더 강하니?)

   **B:** It's a potato, isn't it? (감자야, 그렇지 않니?)

**②　희망 · 기대 표현하기**

I can't wait to see the difference. 나는 빨리 그 차이를 보고 싶어.

■ "I can't wait to …'는 '나는 …이 무척 기다려져.'라는 뜻으로, 희망이나 기대를 말할 때 쓰는 표현이다. to 뒤에는 동사원형이 온다. 이 표현은 'I'm looking forward to -ing'로 바꿔 쓸 수 있다.

**바라거나 기대하는 일 표현하기**

• I can't wait for the cooking class. 나는 요리 수업이 매우 기대가 된다.
• I can't wait to go on a picnic. 나는 소풍가는 것이 매우 기대된다.
• I'm looking forward to meeting my friend. 나는 내 친구를 만나기를 기대하고 있다.
• I really want to visit the museum. 나는 정말로 박물관에 가고 싶다.

**핵심 Check**

2. 다음 우리말과 일치하도록 빈칸에 알맞은 말을 쓰시오.

(1) A: We are going to visit the science museum. (우리는 과학 박물관에 방문할 거야.)

B: I ＿＿＿＿＿ ＿＿＿＿＿ to go there. (나는 빨리 그곳에 가고 싶어.)

(2) A: What are you going to do this Sunday? (이번 주 일요일에 무엇을 할 예정이니?)

B: I'm going to visit my grandparents. I'm ＿＿＿＿ ＿＿＿＿ ＿＿＿＿ ＿＿＿＿ them. (나는 그들을 만나기를 무척 기대하고 있어.)

(3) A: I ＿＿＿＿ ＿＿＿＿ ＿＿＿＿ ＿＿＿＿ ＿＿＿＿ ＿＿＿＿.
(나는 너를 다시 빨리 보고 싶어.)

B: Me too.

**Listen and Speak 1 A**

W: Today we'll make ice cream. ❶Which ❷flavor do you want to make? ❸How about strawberry? First, mix two cups of milk, two cups of heavy cream, and half a cup of sugar. ❹Next, cut five strawberries into small pieces. Then, mix everything together and put it in the freezer. That's it. It's easy to make, isn't it? Why don't you ❺try making it at home?

W: 오늘 우리는 아이스크림을 만들 거예요. 여러분은 어느 맛을 만들고 싶은가요? 딸기는 어때요? 첫째로, 우유 2컵, 헤비 크림 2컵, 설탕 1/2컵을 섞으세요. 다음, 딸기 5개를 작은 조각으로 자르세요. 그 다음에, 모든 것을 섞어서 냉동실에 넣으세요. 이게 다예요. 만들기 쉽죠, 그렇지 않나요? 집에서 아이스크림을 만들어 보는 게 어때요?

❶ 'Which ~?'는 '어느[어떤] ~?'라는 뜻으로 어느 것을 선택하고자 하는지 묻는 표현이다.
❷ flavor: 맛
❸ How about ~? = What about ~?: '~는 어때?'라는 제안을 나타낸다.
❹ Next = Second
❺ try -ing: ~해 보다, cf. try to ~: ~하려고 노력하다

**Check(√) True or False**

(1) The woman explains how to make strawberry ice cream.　　T ☐ F ☐

(2) The woman needs a cup of sugar to make ice cream.　　T ☐ F ☐

**Listen and Speak 2 A**

B: Ms. Jeong, does ❶a glass of water ❷weigh more when there's a fish in it?
W: Yes, it does. We can test it now.
B: But how? We don't have a fish.
W: We can use a finger ❸instead of a fish.
B: How will that work?
W: I'll weigh a glass of water first. Then I will put my finger in the water and weigh it to ❹compare.
B: Oh, ❺I can't wait to see the difference.

B: 정 선생님, 물속에 물고기가 있을 때 물 1잔의 무게가 더 무겁나요?
W: 응, 그렇단다. 우리는 지금 실험해 볼 수 있어.
B: 하지만 어떻게요? 물고기가 없는데요.
W: 우리는 물고기 대신 손가락을 사용할 수 있단다.
B: 어떻게 할 수 있어요?
W: 먼저 물 1잔의 무게를 잴 거야. 그 다음에 비교하기 위해 물속에 손가락을 넣고 무게를 잴 거란다.
B: 아, 차이를 빨리 알고 싶어요.

❶ a glass of: 한 잔의
❷ weigh: 무게를 재다, cf. weight: 무게
❸ instead of: ~ 대신에
❹ compare: 비교하다
❺ I can't wait to ~ = I'm looking forward to -ing: 매우 ~하고 싶다, ~을 기대하다

**Check(√) True or False**

(3) They don't have a fish now.　　T ☐ F ☐

(4) The finger will be used to do an experiment.　　T ☐ F ☐

### Listen and Speak 1 B

B: Yujin, why did you ❶put the eggs in water?

G: I'm ❷picking out the bad eggs.

B: Which eggs are fresh, and which ❸ones are not?

G: Eggs ❹that ❺sink in water are fresh. When eggs ❻float in water, they're not fresh. You shouldn't eat them.

B: That's interesting. Why do the bad eggs float?

G: Because they have gas inside. The gas acts like the air in a balloon.

B: Oh, I see.

❶ put A in B: A를 B에 넣다
❷ pick out: 골라내다
❸ ones = eggs
❹ 주격 관계대명사로 which로 바꾸어 쓸 수 있다.
❺ sink: 가라앉다
❻ float: 뜨다

### Listen and Speak 2 B

King Sejong: It ❶hasn't rained ❷for a long time.

Jang Yeongsil: Yes. The ❸dry season is ❹lasting too long. The farmers are very worried.

King Sejong: We should do something to help ❺them.

Jang Yeongsil: How about making a special clock?

King Sejong: A clock? How will that help?

Jang Yeongsil: The clock will show the time and the seasons. We can use ❻it to prepare for the dry season.

King Sejong: That sounds like a good idea. But who's going to make it?

Jang Yeongsil: I'll ❼give it a try. I know a lot about time and the seasons.

King Sejong: Okay, I can't wait to see your clock.

❶ 현재완료 시제가 쓰였다.
❷ for a long time: 오랫동안
❸ dry season 건기
❹ last: 지속되다
❺ them = farmers
❻ it = the clock
❼ give it a try: 시도해 보다

### Real Life Communication A

Brian: Mina, will you join our tennis club?

Mina: It sounds interesting, but I ❶signed up for a special class this fall.

Brian: Which class did you sign up for?

Mina: I signed up for a magic class. ❷I can't wait to learn new magic ❸tricks there.

Brian: That sounds cool! ❹Have you learned magic tricks before?

Mina: Yes, I learned some before, but I need more practice.

Brian: I hope I can see your magic tricks some day.

❶ sign up for: ~을 신청하다
❷ 'I'm looking forward to learning new magic tricks there.'로 바꾸어 쓸 수 있다.
❸ trick: 마술, 속임수
❹ 현재완료 시제로 경험을 묻고 있다.

### Let's Check

B: What are you reading, Jiwon?

G: I'm reading a book about magic and science.

B: That sounds interesting.

G: Yes. This book ❶introduces 100 magic tricks ❷that use science. I've learned about half of them.

B: That's cool. Can you show me some of the tricks?

G: Sure. I can show you a ❸balloon trick now.

B: Great! I can't wait to see ❹it.

❶ introduce: 소개하다
❷ 관계대명사로 which로 바꾸어 쓸 수 있다.
❸ ballon: 풍선
❹ it = a balloon trick

● 다음 우리말과 일치하도록 빈칸에 알맞은 말을 쓰시오.

### Listen & Speak 1 A

W: Today we'll make ice cream. _____ _____ do you want to make? How about strawberry? _____, mix two cups of milk, two cups of heavy cream, and _____ _____ _____ of sugar. _____, cut five strawberries into small pieces. Then, _____ everything together and put it in the _____. That's it. It's easy to make, isn't it? Why don't you _____ _____ it at home?

### Listen & Speak 1 B

B: Yujin, why did you _____ the eggs in water?

G: I'm _____ _____ the bad eggs.

B: _____ eggs are fresh, and _____ ones are not?

G: Eggs _____ _____ _____ _____ are fresh. When eggs _____ in water, they're not fresh. You shouldn't eat them.

B: That's _____. Why do the bad eggs _____?

G: Because they have gas _____. The gas acts _____ the air in a _____.

B: Oh, I see.

### Listen & Speak 2 A

B: Ms. Jeong, does _____ _____ _____ water _____ more when there's a fish in it?

W: Yes, it does. We can _____ it now.

B: But how? We don't have a fish.

W: We can use a finger _____ _____ a fish.

B: How will that work?

W: I'll _____ a glass of water first. Then I will _____ my finger in the water and weigh it to _____.

B: Oh, I _____ _____ _____ see the difference.

해석

W: 오늘 우리는 아이스크림을 만들 거예요. 여러분은 어느 맛을 만들고 싶은가요? 딸기는 어때요? 첫째로, 우유 2컵, 헤비 크림 2컵, 설탕 1/2컵을 섞으세요. 다음, 딸기 5개를 작은 조각으로 자르세요. 그 다음에, 모든 것을 섞어서 냉동실에 넣으세요. 이게 다예요. 만들기 쉽죠, 그렇지 않나요? 집에서 아이스크림을 만들어 보는 게 어때요?

B: 유진아, 왜 달걀을 물속에 넣었니?

G: 나는 상한 달걀을 골라내는 중이야.

B: 어느 달걀이 신선하고 어느 것이 신선하지 않은 거야?

G: 물에 가라앉는 달걀은 신선해. 달걀이 물에 뜨면, 그건 신선하지 않아. 그것들을 먹으면 안 돼.

B: 그거 재미있다. 상한 달걀은 왜 물에 뜨는 거니?

G: 상한 달걀은 속에 가스가 차기 때문이야. 가스가 풍선 속의 공기 같은 역할을 하거든.

B: 아, 이제 이해했다.

B: 정 선생님, 물속에 물고기가 있을 때 물 1잔의 무게가 더 무겁나요?

W: 응, 그렇단다. 우리는 지금 실험해 볼 수 있어.

B: 하지만 어떻게요? 물고기가 없는데요.

W: 우리는 물고기 대신 손가락을 사용할 수 있단다.

B: 어떻게 할 수 있어요?

W: 먼저 물 1잔의 무게를 잴 거야. 그 다음에 비교하기 위해 물속에 손가락을 넣고 무게를 잴 거란다.

B: 아, 차이를 빨리 알고 싶어요.

### Listen & Speak 2 B

**King Sejong:** It _____ _____ for a long time.

**Jang Yeongsil:** Yes. The dry season is _____ too long. The farmers are very _____.

**King Sejong:** We _____ do something to help them.

**Jang Yeongsil:** How about making a special _____?

**King Sejong:** A clock? How will that help?

**Jang Yeongsil:** The clock will show the time and the _____. We can use it _____ _____ _____ the _____ _____.

**King Sejong:** That sounds _____ a good idea. But who's going to make it?

**Jang Yeongsil:** I'll _____ _____ _____ _____. I know a lot about time and the seasons.

**King Sejong:** Okay, I _____ _____ _____ _____ _____ _____.

### Real Life Communication A

**Brian:** Mina, will you _____ our tennis club?

**Mina:** It sounds interesting, but I _____ _____ _____ a special class this _____.

**Brian:** Which class did you sign up for?

**Mina:** I signed up for a magic class. I can't _____ _____ learn new magic _____ there.

**Brian:** That sounds _____! _____ _____ _____ magic tricks before?

**Mina:** Yes, I learned some before, but I need more _____.

**Brian:** I hope I can see your magic tricks _____ _____.

### Let's Check

**B:** What are you reading, Jiwon?

**G:** I'm reading a book about _____ and _____.

**B:** That sounds _____.

**G:** Yes. This book _____ 100 magic tricks that _____ _____. I've learned about _____ of them.

**B:** That's _____. Can you show me _____ of the tricks?

**G:** Sure. I can show you a _____ trick now.

**B:** Great! I can't _____ _____ see it.

---

**해석**

**King Sejong:** 오랫동안 비가 오지 않는구나.

**Jang Yeongsil:** 그렇습니다. 건기가 너무 오래 계속되고 있습니다. 농부들이 아주 걱정하고 있습니다.

**King Sejong:** 그들을 돕기 위해 뭔가 해야 한다.

**Jang Yeongsil:** 특별한 시계를 만드는 것은 어떨까요?

**King Sejong:** 시계? 그것이 어떻게 도움이 되겠느냐?

**Jang Yeongsil:** 시계는 시간과 계절을 알려줄 겁니다. 건기를 준비하기 위해 시계를 사용할 수 있습니다.

**King Sejong:** 그거 좋은 생각 같구나. 하지만 누가 시계를 만들겠느냐?

**Jang Yeongsil:** 제가 한번 해 보겠습니다. 저는 시간과 계절에 대해 많이 알고 있습니다.

**King Sejong:** 좋다, 네 시계를 빨리 보고 싶구나.

**Brian:** 미나야, 우리 테니스 동아리에 가입할래?

**Mina:** 재미있겠다. 하지만 나는 이번 가을에 특별 수업에 등록했어.

**Brian:** 무슨 수업에 등록했니?

**Mina:** 마술 수업에 등록했어. 거기서 새로운 마술 묘기를 빨리 배우고 싶어.

**Brian:** 그거 재미있겠다! 전에 마술 묘기를 배운 적이 있니?

**Mina:** 응, 전에 몇 가지 배웠어, 하지만 더 연습을 해야 해.

**Brian:** 언젠가 네 마술 묘기를 볼 수 있길 바라.

**B:** 지원아, 뭘 읽고 있니?

**G:** 마술과 과학에 관한 책을 읽고 있어.

**B:** 그거 재미있겠다.

**G:** 응. 이 책은 과학을 사용하는 100가지 마술을 소개하고 있어. 나는 그 중에 절반 정도를 익혔어.

**B:** 멋지다. 마술 중 몇 가지를 보여줄 수 있니?

**G:** 물론이지. 지금 풍선 마술을 보여줄 수 있어.

**B:** 멋지다! 빨리 보고 싶어.

**[01~02]** 다음 대화를 읽고 물음에 답하시오.

> Jaemin: Ms. Jeong, does a glass of water @weigh more when there's a fish in it?
>
> Ms. Jeong: Yes, it ⓑdoes. We can test it now.
>
> Jaemin: But how? We don't have a fish.
>
> Ms. Jeong: We can use a finger ⓒinstead of a fish.
>
> Jaemin: How will that work?
>
> Ms. Jeong: I'll weigh a glass of water first. Then I will put my finger in the water and weigh it ⓓto compare.
>
> Jaemin: Oh, I can't wait to ⓔseeing the difference.

**01** 위 대화의 밑줄 친 @~ⓔ 중 어법상 어색한 것을 찾아 바르게 고치시오.

➡ _____

**02** 위 대화의 내용과 일치하지 않는 것은?

① 물속에 물고기가 있을 때 물 한 잔의 무게는 더 무겁다.

② 정 선생님과 재민이는 물고기 대신 손가락으로 실험하려고 한다.

③ 정 선생님은 물 한 잔의 무게를 잴 것이다.

④ 물 한 잔의 무게를 잰 후 물속에 손가락을 넣고 무게를 잴 것이다.

⑤ 재민이는 그 실험의 결과를 이미 알고 있다.

**[03~04]** 다음 대화를 읽고 물음에 답하시오.

> Brian: Mina, will you join our tennis club?
>
> Mina: It sounds interesting, but I signed up for a special class this fall.
>
> Brian: (A)무슨 수업에 등록했니? (for, which)
>
> Mina: I signed up for a magic class. I can't wait to learn new magic tricks there.
>
> Brian: That sounds cool! Have you learned magic tricks before?
>
> Mina: Yes, I learned some before, but I need more practice.
>
> Brian: I hope I can see your magic tricks some day.

**03** 위 대화의 밑줄 친 (A)의 우리말을 주어진 단어를 사용하여 영작하시오.

➡ _____

**04** 위 대화에서 알 수 있는 Mina의 심경으로 적절한 것은?

① excited          ② worried          ③ lonely

④ upset            ⑤ depressed

[01~03] 다음 글을 읽고 물음에 답하시오.

Jane: Today we'll make ice cream. Which flavor do you want to make? How about strawberry? First, mix two cups of milk, two cups of heavy cream, and half a cup of sugar. Next, cut five strawberries into small pieces. Then, mix everything together and put it in the freezer. That's it. It's easy to make, (A)그렇지 않나요? Why don't you try making it at home?

**서답형**

**01** 위 글의 밑줄 친 (A)의 우리말을 두 단어를 사용하여 영작하시오.

➡ _____

**서답형**

**02** 위 글에서 언급한 아이스크림을 만들기 위한 준비물로서 바르지 <u>않은</u> 것은?

**중요**

**03** 위 글의 내용과 일치하지 <u>않는</u> 것은?

① Jane은 딸기 아이스크림 만드는 법을 설명하고 있다.

② 아이스크림을 만들기 위해 우유, 헤비 크림, 설탕, 딸기가 필요하다.

③ 딸기 5개를 작은 조각으로 잘라야 한다.

④ 모든 재료를 섞어서 냉동실에 넣어야 한다.

⑤ Jane은 집에서는 아이스크림을 만들지 않는다.

[04~06] 다음 대화를 읽고 물음에 답하시오.

Brian: Yujin, why did you put the eggs in water?

Yujin: I'm picking out the bad eggs.

Brian: Which eggs are fresh, and (A)[which / what] ones are not?

Yujin: Eggs that sink in water (B)[is / are] fresh. When eggs float in water, they're not fresh. You shouldn't eat (D)them.

Brian: That's interesting. Why do the bad eggs float?

Yujin: (C)[Because / Because of] they have gas inside. The gas acts like the air in a balloon.

Brian: Oh, I see.

**04** 위 대화의 괄호 (A)~(C)에 들어갈 말로 바르게 짝지어진 것은?

① which – is – Because

② which – are – Because of

③ which – are – Because

④ what – are – Because of

⑤ what – is – Because

**서답형**

**05** 위 대화의 밑줄 친 (D)them이 가리키는 것을 우리말로 쓰시오.

➡ _____

**중요**

**06** 위 대화의 내용과 일치하지 <u>않는</u> 것은?

① 유진이는 상한 달걀을 골라내는 중이다.

② 물에 가라앉는 달걀은 신선한 것이다.

③ 달걀이 물에 뜨면 신선하지 않은 것이다.

④ 상한 달걀은 가스를 내뿜는다.

⑤ 가스가 풍선 속의 공기 같은 역할을 한다.

[07~08] 다음 대화를 읽고 물음에 답하시오.

King Sejong: It hasn't rained for a long time.

Jang Yeongsil: Yes. The dry season is lasting too long. The farmers are very worried.

King Sejong: (A) We should do something to help them.

Jang Yeongsil: (B) How about making a special clock?

King Sejong: (C) A clock? How will that help?

Jang Yeongsil: (D) We can use it to prepare for the dry season.

King Sejong: (E) That sounds like a good idea. But who's going to make it?

Jang Yeongsil: I'll give it a try. I know a lot about time and the seasons.

King Sejong: Okay, I can't wait to see your clock.

**07** 위 대화의 (A)~(E) 중 주어진 문장이 들어가기에 적절한 곳은?

> The clock will show the time and the seasons.

① (A)　② (B)　③ (C)　④ (D)　⑤ (E)

**08** 위 대화를 읽고 대답할 수 <u>없는</u> 것은?

① What's the matter?

② What does Jang Yeongsil suggest?

③ Why does Jang Yeongsil want to make a special clock?

④ What does Jang Yeongsil know about a lot?

⑤ What does King Sejong do to finish the dry season?

[09~10] 다음 대화를 읽고 물음에 답하시오.

Brian: Mina, will you join our tennis club?

Mina: It sounds interesting, but I signed up for a special class this fall.

Brian: Which class did you sign up for?

Mina: I signed up for a magic class. I can't wait to learn new magic tricks there.

Brian: ＿＿＿＿(A)＿＿＿＿ Have you learned magic tricks before?

Mina: Yes, I learned some before, but I need more practice.

Brian: I hope I can see your magic tricks some day.

**09** 위 대화의 빈칸 (A)에 들어갈 말로 적절한 것은?

① I'm sorry to hear that.

② That sounds cool!

③ Take it easy.

④ I don't think so.

⑤ It's not your fault.

**10** 위 대화를 읽고 대답할 수 <u>없는</u> 것은?

① Which class did Mina sign up for this fall?

② Why couldn't Mina join the tennis club?

③ What does Mina want to learn in the magic class?

④ Has Mina learned magic tricks before?

⑤ How long has Mina practiced magic tricks?

[01~03] 다음 대화를 읽고 물음에 답하시오.

Jaemin: Ms. Jeong, does a glass of water weigh more when there's a fish in it?
Ms. Jeong: Yes, it does. We can test it now.
Jaemin: But how? We don't have a fish.
Ms. Jeong: We can use a finger instead of a fish.
Jaemin: How will that work?
Ms. Jeong: I'll weigh a glass of water first. Then I will put my finger in the water and weigh it to compare.
Jaemin: Oh, (A)차이를 빨리 알고 싶어요.

**01** 위 대화의 밑줄 친 (A)의 우리말을 〈보기〉에 주어진 모든 단어들을 배열하여 영작하시오.

보기
to / I / difference / wait / can't / see / the

➡ _____

**02** What will Ms. Jeong use instead of a fish?

➡ _____

**03** What do Ms. Jeong and Jaemin want to see through the experiment?

A: They want to see whether _____
_____ .

**04** 다음 대화에서 (A)~(E)를 자연스럽게 이어지도록 순서대로 배열하시오.

King Sejong: It hasn't rained for a long time.
Jang Yeongsil: Yes. The dry season is lasting too long. The farmers are very worried.
King Sejong: We should do something to help them.

(A) I'll give it a try. I know a lot about time and the seasons.
(B) A clock? How will that help?
(C) That sounds like a good idea. But who's going to make it?
(D) How about making a special clock?
(E) The clock will show the time and the seasons. We can use it to prepare for the dry season.

King Sejong: Okay, I can't wait to see your clock.

➡ _____

[05~06] 다음 글을 읽고 물음에 답하시오.

Jane: Today we'll make ice cream. Which flavor do you want to make? How about strawberry? First, mix two cups of milk, two cups of heavy cream, and half a cup of sugar. Next, cut five strawberries into small pieces. Then, mix everything together and put it in the freezer. That's it. It's easy to make, isn't it? Why don't you try making it at home?

**05** According to Jane, what do you need to prepare for making strawberry ice cream?

➡ _____

**06** What should you do after cutting the strawberries into small pieces?

➡ _____
_____

# Grammar

## ① 가주어 It

> * **It** is good **to meet** him. 그를 만나는 것은 좋다.
> * **It** is wrong **to speak** ill of your friends. 친구에 관해 나쁘게 말하는 것은 옳지 않다.

■ to부정사구가 주어로 쓰여 주어가 길어진 경우, 주어부를 문장의 맨 뒤로 보내고 이 자리에 It을 쓰는 것이 가주어 It이다. 명사절 접속사가 이끄는 that절 역시 이에 해당한다.

- **To keep** your promise is important.
  = **It** is important **to keep** your promise. 너의 약속을 지키는 것은 중요하다.

- **That he broke his leg** was surprising.
  = **It** was surprising **that** he broke his leg. 그의 다리가 부러졌다는 것은 놀라웠다.

■ 가주어 It은 따로 해석하지 않으며 to부정사구를 주어로 해석해야 한다. to부정사구의 부정은 'not+to V'로 표기한다.

- **It** is good **not to make** noises in the library. 도서관에서는 소음을 내지 않는 것이 좋다.

- **It** is bad **not to say** sorry when you do wrong. 네가 잘못을 했을 때 미안하다고 말하지 않는 것은 나빠.

■ 진주어 to부정사의 행위 주체를 명시하고 싶은 경우, 의미상의 주어로 'for/of+목적격'을 사용한다. 'for+목적격'은 '상황에 대한 의견'을 나타내는 형용사 뒤에서, 'of+목적격'은 '사람의 성격'을 나타내는 형용사 뒤에서 쓰인다.

- **It** is kind **of** her **to help** you. 그녀가 너를 도와주는 것은 친절해.

- **It** is not safe **for** you **to go** outside alone. 네가 혼자 밖으로 나가는 것은 안전하지 않아.

### 핵심 Check

**1.** 다음 우리말과 일치하도록 빈칸에 알맞은 말을 쓰시오.

(1) 식물을 돌보는 것은 쉽지 않다.
➡ It is not easy ＿＿＿ ＿＿＿ ＿＿＿ of plants.

(2) 너를 매일 만나는 것은 좋아.
➡ It is nice ＿＿＿ ＿＿＿ you every day.

(3) 우리가 침착함을 유지하는 것은 중요해.
➡ It is important ＿＿＿ ＿＿＿ ＿＿＿ ＿＿＿ calm.

## ② How come ...?

> • **How come** you are angry with me? 도대체 너는 왜 내게 화가 났니?
>
> • **How come** she came late? 그녀는 도대체 왜 늦었니?

■ 의문사 why와 how come은 의미는 비슷하지만 어순상의 차이를 보인다. 'How come+주어+동사 …?'로 쓰여 '도대체 왜 …?'라는 의미이지만, why는 'Why+동사+주어 …?'의 어순으로 쓰인다.

• **How come** you bought this? 도대체 이걸 왜 산 거야?

**Why** did you buy this? 이것을 왜 산 거니?

**How come** he made this cake? 도대체 왜 그가 이 케이크를 만든 거야?

**Why** did he make this cake? 그는 왜 이 케이크를 만든 거야?

**How come** she looked disappointed? 그녀는 도대체 왜 실망한 것처럼 보였니?

**Why** did she look disappointed? 그녀는 왜 실망한 것처럼 보였니?

**How come** you are here? 도대체 네가 왜 여기에 있는 거야?

**Why** are you here? 너는 왜 여기에 있니?

**How come** you sent the message like that? 도대체 너는 왜 그런 메시지를 보낸 거야?

**Why** did you send the message like that? 왜 너는 그런 메시지를 보냈니?

### 핵심 Check

2. 다음 우리말을 영어로 쓰시오.

(1) 도대체 왜 내게 거짓말을 했니?

➡ _____ _____ you lied to me?

(2) 왜 그 소년이 울고 있니?

➡ _____ is the boy crying?

(3) 도대체 왜 그가 그런 말을 했니?

➡ _____ _____ he said things like that?

(4) 도대체 왜 그를 초대했니?

➡ _____ _____ you invited him?

**01** 다음 문장에서 어법상 <u>어색한</u> 부분을 바르게 고쳐 쓰시오.

(1) It was difficult stop my bad habit.

_____ ➡ _____

(2) It is impossible of you to finish the project.

_____ ➡ _____

(3) How come did you meet her?

_____ ➡ _____

(4) How came he was with you?

_____ ➡ _____

**02** 다음 우리말과 일치하도록 빈칸에 알맞은 말을 쓰시오.

(1) 도대체 왜 그는 물을 그렇게 많이 마시는 거야?

➡ How come _____ _____ so much water?

(2) 왜 너는 운동을 열심히 하니?

➡ Why _____ _____ _____ hard?

(3) 도대체 왜 그녀가 슬퍼 보이는 거지?

➡ How come _____ _____ sad?

(4) 왜 너는 그렇게 빨리 달렸니?

➡ Why _____ _____ _____ so fast?

**03** 주어진 단어를 바르게 배열하여 다음 우리말을 영어로 쓰시오. 필요하다면 단어를 추가하시오.

(1) 운동을 규칙적으로 하는 것은 매우 중요해.

(exercise / regularly / important / is / it / very)

➡ _____

(2) 놀이공원에 가는 것은 신난다.

(it / the amusement park / exciting / to / go / is)

➡ _____

(3) 친구들에게 정직한 것은 중요해.

(your friends / important / honest / be / is / it / with)

➡ _____

(4) 그것을 설명하는 것은 나의 일이야. (it / it / explain / my job / is )

➡ _____

**01** 다음 빈칸에 들어갈 말로 가장 적절한 것은?

> It is good _____ early in the morning.

① wake up      ② to wake up
③ woke up      ④ to waking up
⑤ woken up

**02** 다음 우리말을 영어로 바르게 옮긴 것은?

> 도대체 왜 그녀는 우리에게 다시 돌아온 거야?

① Why is she coming back to us?
② Why is she returning to us?
③ How come she came back to us?
④ How come did she come back to us?
⑤ How came she came back to us?

**03** 다음 중 빈칸에 들어갈 말이 다른 하나는?

① It was wise _____ him to say sorry.
② It is generous _____ her to lend us money.
③ It is rude _____ you to talk like that to your elders.
④ It is easy _____ me to solve this problem.
⑤ It was careful _____ them to keep their valuables in the safe.

**서답형**

**04** 주어진 단어를 활용하여 다음 우리말을 영어로 쓰시오.

> 외국어를 배우는 것은 재미있다.
> (fun / it)

➡ _____

**05** 다음 주어진 문장의 밑줄 친 부분과 쓰임이 같은 것은?

> It is exciting to ride a bike with friends.

① The dog was barking at us to protect his house.
② It is surprising to see you here.
③ Is there anything to wear?
④ The man went into his room to take a rest.
⑤ We want you to do your best.

**06** 다음 빈칸에 들어갈 말이 바르게 짝지어진 것은?

> • It is amazing _____ the plants grow in our garden.
> • _____ he jogs every morning?

① see – Why         ② to see – Why
③ saw – Why         ④ to see – How come
⑤ to seeing – How come

**07** 다음 중 빈칸에 들어갈 말이 다른 하나는?

① _____ she took him to the store?
② _____ he broke his promise?
③ _____ we didn't take a bus?
④ _____ they didn't come?
⑤ _____ are we going to visit them?

**서답형**

**08** 다음 빈칸에 알맞은 말을 쓰시오.

> To read books is very fun.
> ➡ It is very fun _____ _____ _____.

**09** 주어진 단어를 바르게 배열하여 다음 우리말을 영어로 쓸 때 다섯 번째로 오는 단어는?

> 인사하는 방법을 아는 것은 좋다.
> (hello / nice / how / it / to / is / say / to / know)

① to　　　　② nice　　　　③ say
④ know　　　⑤ hello

**10** 다음 중 밑줄 친 부분의 쓰임이 <u>다른</u> 하나는?

① <u>It</u> is true that he succeeded in climbing the mountain.
② <u>It</u> was good to hear the news from her.
③ <u>It</u> is cloudy and windy.
④ <u>It</u> is fun to see movies.
⑤ <u>It</u> was wrong to make fun of your friend.

**11** 다음 중 어법상 바르지 <u>않은</u> 것은?

① How come you woke up so late?
② It is true that he made the robot.
③ That is surprising to see you play the piano.
④ It will be difficult for you to understand the book.
⑤ It was not easy to talk with her.

**12** 다음 중 어법상 바르지 <u>않은</u> 것은?

> ①It was ②careless ③for them ④to tell their children something ⑤like that.

①　　　②　　　③　　　④　　　⑤

**13** 주어진 단어를 활용하여 다음 우리말을 영어로 쓰시오.

> 도대체 그녀는 왜 그 재킷을 산 거야?
> (how / the jacket)

➡ _____

**14** 다음 중 우리말로 옮긴 것이 바르지 <u>않은</u> 것은?

① 도대체 왜 너는 내 말을 안 들은 거니?
　→ How come you didn't listen to me?
② 네가 그 음악을 듣는 것은 놀랍다.
　→ It is surprising for you to hear the music.
③ 그 단어들의 의미를 찾는 것은 도움이 될 거야.
　→ It will be helpful to find the meanings of the words.
④ 그 일에 너를 추천하는 것은 나의 생각이 아니었어.
　→ To recommend you for the job was not my idea.
⑤ 내가 너를 막는 것은 불가능했어.
　→ It was impossible of me to stop you.

**15** 다음 빈칸에 들어갈 말로 가장 적절한 것은?

> _____ he broke into someone's house?

① Why　　　② What　　　③ When
④ How come　⑤ Where

**16** 주어진 단어를 바르게 배열하여 다음 우리말을 영어로 쓰시오. 필요하다면 단어를 추가하시오.

> 걷는 동안 휴대 전화기를 사용하지 않는 것이 중요하다.
> (important / your phone / walking / to / it / use / is / while)

➡ _____

**서답형**

**17** 다음 빈칸에 알맞은 말을 쓰시오.

> 도대체 그녀는 왜 어제 떠난 거야?
> ➡ How come _____ _____ yesterday?

**18** 다음 중 빈칸에 들어갈 말이 바르게 짝지어진 것은?

> • It is wise _____ her to go with you to the hospital.
> • It is necessary _____ they come here on time.

① to – to      ② for – to
③ of – that     ④ of – to
⑤ for – that

**19** 다음 우리말을 영어로 바르게 옮긴 것을 모두 고르시오.

> 부주의하게 운전하는 것은 위험하다.

① It is careless to drive dangerously.
② It is dangerous drive carelessly.
③ To drive carelessly is dangerous.
④ It is dangerous to drive carelessly.
⑤ It is careless drive dangerously.

**20** 다음 괄호 안의 단어를 어법에 맞게 쓸 때 형태가 다른 하나는?

① It is kind of him (help) you.
② It is rude of you (say) such words.
③ It is good at (build) nests on trees.
④ It is bad for you (use) someone's stuff without asking.
⑤ It is necessary for me (do) my homework.

**서답형**

**21** 다음 문장과 같은 의미의 문장을 쓰시오.

> To tell a stranger where you live is dangerous.

➡ _____

**22** 다음 중 빈칸에 들어갈 말이 바르게 짝지어진 것은?

> A: Your room is so messy. _____ you didn't clean your room?
> B: It's because I was too busy. It was impossible _____ me to clean the room.

① Why – that      ② Why – of
③ How come – for   ④ How come – of
⑤ How come – that

**23** 다음 중 어법상 옳은 것은?

① It is fun hear him talking about interesting stories.
② How come did you lose your weight?
③ It is brave for you to make the decision.
④ Why you weren't doing the laundry?
⑤ It is stupid of her to behave like that in front of so many people.

**서답형**

**24** 다음 주어진 단어를 활용하여 다음 문장과 같은 의미의 문장을 쓰시오.

> Why did you call me? (how)

➡ _____

**01** 주어진 단어를 활용하여 다음 우리말을 영어로 쓰시오.

> 헬멧을 쓰지 않는 것은 위험하다.
> (it / your / wear)

➡ _____

**02** 다음 빈칸에 알맞은 말을 쓰시오.

(1) 왜 그녀는 지금 너를 쳐다보고 있는 거야?

   ➡ How come _____ _____ _____
      at you now?

(2) 왜 너는 그 아이들을 초대한 거니?

   ➡ Why _____ _____ _____ the
      children?

(3) 도대체 왜 그 선생님은 우리에게 할 일을 그렇게 많이 주시는 거야?

   ➡ How come _____ _____
      us so many things to do?

(4) 왜 우리는 그 식당으로 가고 있는 거야?

   ➡ How come _____ _____
      to the restaurant?

(5) 왜 너는 모자를 쓰고 있는 거니?

   ➡ Why _____ _____ _____ a hat?

**03** 다음 문장과 같은 의미의 문장을 완성하시오.

(1) To travel abroad is exciting.

   ➡ It _____.

(2) To read this novel is not easy.

   ➡ It _____.

(3) It is useful to know how to use this machine.

   ➡ To _____.

**04** 주어진 단어를 바르게 배열하여 다음 우리말을 영어로 쓰시오. 필요하다면 단어를 추가하시오.

> 네가 그렇게 말한 것은 어리석었어.
> (you / it / say / stupid / was / so / to)

➡ _____

**05** 주어진 단어를 활용하여 다음 문장과 같은 의미의 문장을 쓰시오.

> Why did you put your wallet on the table?
> (how)

➡ _____

**06** 다음 빈칸에 알맞은 말을 쓰시오.

> 내가 그 산을 오르는 것이 가능해?
> ➡ Is it possible _____ _____ _____
> _____ up the mountain?

**07** 주어진 단어를 활용하여 다음 대화를 영어로 쓰시오.

> A: _____ (how / today)
> B: I am going to meet her today because I don't have any free time tomorrow.

➡ _____

**08** 다음 빈칸에 알맞은 말을 쓰시오.

> It is surprising _____ he didn't call you.

**9** 다음 빈칸에 적절한 말을 쓰시오.

> _____ _____ you made her do the dishes?
>
> = _____ did you make her do the dishes?

**10** 다음 대화의 빈칸에 알맞은 말을 쓰시오.

> A: Is it easy _____?
> B: I don't think so. To form good habits is not easy.

➡ _____

**11** 주어진 단어를 활용하여 다음 대화를 영어로 쓰시오.

> A: 도대체 왜 그녀는 나에게 사과하지 않는 거야? (how / say sorry)
> B: 그녀가 너에게 미안하다고 말하는 것은 쉽지 않다고 생각해. (it / think)

A: _____

B: _____

**12** 다음 빈칸에 들어갈 알맞은 말을 쓰시오.

> It was nice _____ you to send me a birthday card.

**13** 다음 문장에서 어법상 틀린 것을 바르게 고쳐 문장을 다시 쓰시오.

> How come did you forget to bring the book?

➡ _____

**14** 주어진 단어를 바르게 배열하여 다음 우리말을 영어로 쓰시오. 필요하다면 단어를 추가하시오.

> 그가 너에게 자기의 옷을 빌려준 것은 정말 관대했어.
> (his clothes / him / lend / generous / was / to / it / you)

➡ _____

**15** 주어진 단어를 활용하여 다음 문장과 같은 의미의 문장을 쓰시오.

> Why did you book the restaurant?
> (how)

➡ _____

**16** 다음 빈칸에 알맞은 말을 쓰시오.

> A: Was it fun to watch the movie?
> B: Yes. _____ was really fun.

➡ _____

**17** 다음 빈칸에 알맞은 말을 쓰시오.

> 너는 왜 John을 돕지 않았니?
> = _____ _____ you didn't help John?
> = _____ _____ _____ help John?

**18** 주어진 단어를 활용하여 다음 대화의 우리말을 영어로 쓰시오.

> A: 너는 왜 공부를 열심히 하는 거야? (how)
> B: 공부를 열심히 하는 것은 나를 행복하게 해. (make me happy / it)

A: _____

B: _____

# Reading

교과서

## The Super Science Magic Show

**Jina:** Welcome to the Super Science Magic Show! It's always exciting to see magic tricks. And it's more exciting to find out the secrets behind them. Some people think the secret of magic is science. Today, Ken, a member of the School Magic Club, will use science to perform his tricks. Which tricks will he show us? I can't wait to see them.

### The Amazing Rising Water

**Ken:** Hello, everyone. Today, I'm going to show you something amazing. Here's a dish with water in it. Now, I'll put a candle in the middle of the dish. Next, I'll light the candle and cover it with a glass. "Abracadabra!"

**Jina:** Look at the water! How come it rose into the glass?

**Ken:** Air expands when it gets hot and creates higher pressure. When it gets cold, air contracts and creates lower pressure. When the flame burnt out, the air inside the glass cooled down. As the air cooled down, the air pressure dropped. So the air outside the glass was at a higher pressure. It pushed the water into the glass.

magic 마술의
trick 속임수, 마술, 묘기
secret 비밀
candle 초, 양초
abracadabra 아브라카다브라 (주문)
expand 팽창하다
pressure 압력
contract 수축하다
flame 불꽃
burn out 타 버리다
cool down 식다, 차가워지다

📎 **확인문제**

● 다음 문장이 본문의 내용과 일치하면 T, 일치하지 않으면 F를 쓰시오.

1  Ken belongs to the School Magic Club. ☐

2  Ken will show students some tricks without using science. ☐

3  Air expands when it gets hot and creates lower pressure. ☐

4  As the air cooled down, the air pressure rose. ☐

5  The air inside the glass cooled down because the flame burnt out. ☐

## The Secret of the Underlined{Disappearing} Water
현재분사(사라지는)

**Ken:** Now, I'm going to fill one of these cups with water. I will move
fill A with B: A를 B로 채우다

them around to confuse you. Jina, which cup has the water in it?
cups          to부정사의 부사적 용법 중 목적(~하기 위해서)

**Jina:** That's easy! It's the middle one.

**Ken:** Okay, let's check. See? No water.
= There is no water

**Jina:** Show me the other cups.
4형식 (show+사람+사물)

**Ken:** See? There's no water.

**Jina:** Wow! How come the water disappeared?
How come+주어+동사 ~?

**Ken:** Before the trick, I put a special material into one of the cups. The
put A into B: A를 B 안에 넣다

material absorbed the water and turned it into jelly. Then the jelly
the water

stuck to the bottom. If you want to try this trick, it's necessary to
stick(들러붙다)의 과거                              진주어 to부정사

use cups that you can't see through.
목적격 관계대명사

**Jina:** Thank you for your great performance. It was really amazing!
현재분사(놀라움을 유발하는)

---

confuse 혼동하게 하다

material 물질, 재료

absorb 흡수하다

turn A into B A를 B로 바꾸다

bottom 바닥

necessary 필요한, 필연적인

see through 속을 들여다보다, 꿰뚫어
보다

---

### 확인문제

● 다음 문장이 본문의 내용과 일치하면 T, 일치하지 <u>않으면</u> F를 쓰시오.

1  Ken moved cups around including the one which had water in it. ☐

2  Jina thought that the cup which was in the middle had water. ☐

3  There was no water in all of the cups. ☐

4  The jelly didn't stick to the bottom of the cup. ☐

5  You need cups that can't be seen through to do the trick. ☐

6  Jina thought the performance that Ken showed was amazing. ☐

● 우리말을 참고하여 빈칸에 알맞은 말을 쓰시오.

**1** Jina: _____ _____ the Super Science Magic Show!

**2** _____ always _____ _____ _____ magic tricks.

**3** And it's more exciting _____ _____ _____ the secrets _____ them.

**4** Some people think the secret of magic _____ _____.

**5** Today, Ken, a member of the School Magic Club, _____ _____ _____ _____ _____ his tricks.

**6** Which tricks _____ he _____ _____? I can't wait _____ _____ _____.

**7** Ken: Hello, everyone. Today, I'm going _____ _____ _____ something amazing.

**8** Here's a dish _____ _____ _____ _____.

**9** Now, I'll _____ _____ _____ in the middle of the dish.

**10** Next, I'll _____ the candle and _____ _____ _____ a glass. "Abracadabra!"

**11** Jina: Look _____ the water! _____ _____ it _____ _____ the glass?

**12** Ken: Air _____ when it gets _____ and creates _____ _____.

**13** When it _____ _____, air _____ and creates _____ _____.

**14** When the flame _____ _____, the air inside the glass _____ _____.

**15** As the air _____ _____, the air pressure _____.

**1** 지나: 특별 과학 마술 쇼에 오신 것을 환영합니다!

**2** 마술을 보는 것은 항상 신나는 일입니다.

**3** 그리고 마술 뒤에 숨겨진 비밀을 알아내는 것은 더 신나는 일입니다.

**4** 어떤 사람들은 마술의 비밀이 과학이라고 생각합니다.

**5** 오늘 학교 마술 동아리 회원인 Ken은 마술을 수행하기 위해 과학을 사용할 것입니다.

**6** 그는 우리에게 어떤 마술을 보여 줄까요? 무척 기다려지는군요.

**7** Ken: 안녕하세요, 여러분. 오늘, 저는 여러분에게 놀라운 무언가를 보여 주려고 합니다.

**8** 여기에 물이 담긴 접시가 있습니다.

**9** 이제, 저는 접시 한가운데에 초를 놓을 것입니다.

**10** 그다음에 초를 켜고 유리컵으로 초를 덮어 보겠습니다. "아브라카다브라!"

**11** 지나: 물을 보세요! 어째서 물이 유리컵 속으로 올라간 거지요?

**12** Ken: 공기가 뜨거워지면 팽창해서, 더 높은 압력을 만듭니다.

**13** 공기가 차가워지면 수축해서, 더 낮은 압력을 만듭니다.

**14** 불꽃이 다 타 버렸을 때, 유리컵 속의 공기는 식어 버렸습니다.

**15** 공기가 식었으므로, 기압이 낮아졌습니다.

16  So the air outside the glass _____ _____ _____
_____.

17  It _____ the water _____ the glass.

18  Ken: Now, I'm going _____ _____ _____ _____
_____ _____ with water.

19  I will move _____ _____ _____ _____ you.

20  Jina, _____ _____ has the water in it?

21  Jina: That's easy! _____ the middle _____.

22  Ken: Okay, _____ _____. See? No water.

23  Jina: Show _____ _____ _____ _____.

24  Ken: See? There's _____ _____.

25  Jina: Wow! _____ _____ the water _____?

26  Ken: _____ the trick, I _____ a special material _____
one of _____ _____.

27  The material _____ the water and _____ _____ _____
jelly.

28  Then the jelly _____ _____ _____ _____.

29  If you want to try this trick, it's _____ _____ _____ cups
_____ you can't see through.

30  Jina: Thank you _____ your great _____. It was really
_____!

---

16  그래서 유리컵 밖의 공기 압력
이 더 높아졌습니다.

17  높아진 압력의 공기가 물을 밀
어서 유리컵으로 들어가게 된
것입니다.

18  Ken: 이제, 이 컵들 중 하나를
물로 채워 보겠습니다.

19  여러분을 헷갈리게 하려고 이
컵들을 섞어 보겠습니다.

20  지나, 어떤 컵에 물이 있을까요?

21  지나: 쉽네요! 가운데 컵이에요.

22  Ken: 좋습니다, 확인해 봅시다.
보셨죠? 물이 없군요.

23  지나: 다른 컵들도 보여 주세요.

24  Ken: 보셨죠? 물이 없네요.

25  지나: 왜 어째서 물이 사라진 거죠?

26  Ken: 마술 전에, 저는 특별한 물
질을 컵 하나에 넣어 두었습니다.

27  그 물질은 물을 흡수하고, 그것
을 젤리로 변하게 했습니다.

28  그리고 나서 젤리는 컵 바닥에
달라붙었습니다.

29  여러분이 이 마술을 해 보고자
한다면, 속을 들여다볼 수 없는
컵을 사용해야 합니다.

30  지나: 멋진 공연 고맙습니다. 정
말 놀라웠어요!

• 우리말을 참고하여 본문을 영작하시오.

**1** 지나: 특별 과학 마술 쇼에 오신 것을 환영합니다!

➡ _____

**2** 마술을 보는 것은 항상 신나는 일입니다.

➡ _____

**3** 그리고 마술 뒤에 숨겨진 비밀을 알아내는 것은 더 신나는 일입니다.

➡ _____

**4** 어떤 사람들은 마술의 비밀이 과학이라고 생각합니다.

➡ _____

**5** 오늘 학교 마술 동아리 회원인 Ken은 마술을 수행하기 위해 과학을 사용할 것입니다.

➡ _____

**6** 그는 우리에게 어떤 마술을 보여 줄까요? 무척 기다려지는군요.

➡ _____

**7** Ken: 안녕하세요, 여러분. 오늘, 저는 여러분에게 놀라운 무언가를 보여 주려고 합니다.

➡ _____

**8** 여기에 물이 담긴 접시가 있습니다.

➡ _____

**9** 이제, 저는 접시 한가운데에 초를 놓을 것입니다.

➡ _____

**10** 그다음에 초를 켜고 유리컵으로 초를 덮어 보겠습니다. "아브라카다브라!"

➡ _____

**11** 지나: 물을 보세요! 어째서 물이 유리컵 속으로 올라간 거지요?

➡ _____

**12** Ken: 공기가 뜨거워지면 팽창해서, 더 높은 압력을 만듭니다.

➡ _____

**13** 공기가 차가워지면 수축해서, 더 낮은 압력을 만듭니다.

➡ _____

**14** 불꽃이 다 타 버렸을 때, 유리컵 속의 공기는 식어 버렸습니다.

➡ _____

**15** 공기가 식었으므로, 기압이 낮아졌습니다.

➡ _____

**16** 그래서 유리컵 밖의 공기 압력이 더 높아졌습니다.

➡ _____

**17** 높아진 압력의 공기가 물을 밀어서 유리컵으로 들어가게 된 것입니다.

➡ _____

**18** Ken: 이제, 이 컵들 중 하나를 물로 채워 보겠습니다.

➡ _____

**19** 여러분을 헷갈리게 하려고 이 컵들을 섞어 보겠습니다.

➡ _____

**20** 지나, 어떤 컵에 물이 있을까요?

➡ _____

**21** 지나: 쉽네요! 가운데 컵이에요.

➡ _____

**22** Ken: 좋습니다, 확인해 봅시다. 보셨죠? 물이 없군요.

➡ _____

**23** 지나: 다른 컵들도 보여 주세요.

➡ _____

**24** Ken: 보셨죠? 물이 없네요.

➡ _____

**25** 지나: 와! 어째서 물이 사라진 거죠?

➡ _____

**26** Ken: 마술 전에, 저는 특별한 물질을 컵 하나에 넣어 두었습니다.

➡ _____

**27** 그 물질은 물을 흡수하고, 그것을 젤리로 변하게 했습니다.

➡ _____

**28** 그러고 나서 젤리는 컵 바닥에 달라붙었습니다.

➡ _____

**29** 여러분이 이 마술을 해 보고자 한다면, 속을 들여다볼 수 없는 컵을 사용해야 합니다.

➡ _____

**30** 지나: 멋진 공연 고맙습니다. 정말 놀라웠어요!

➡ _____

**[01~03]** 다음 글을 읽고 물음에 답하시오.

Jina: Welcome (A)_____ the Super Science Magic Show! It's always exciting to see magic tricks. And it's more exciting to find out the secrets behind them. Some people think the secret of magic is science. Today, Ken, a member of the School Magic Club, will use science to perform his tricks. Which tricks will he show us? I can't wait to see them.

**01** 다음 중 빈칸 (A)에 들어갈 말로 가장 적절한 것은?

① for    ② to    ③ in
④ at    ⑤ about

**02** What does Jina want to talk about?

① Science that uses magic.
② Magic used by scientists.
③ Magic using science.
④ Magical things around us.
⑤ The most surprising thing in the world.

서답형

**03** Who is Ken? Answer in English with a full sentence.

➡ _____

**[04~09]** 다음 글을 읽고 물음에 답하시오.

Ken: Hello, everyone. Today, I'm going to show you something amazing. Here's a dish with water in it. Now, I'll put a candle in the middle of the dish. Next, I'll light the candle and cover it with a glass. "Abracadabra!"

Jina: Look at the water! How come it ①rose into the glass?

Ken: Air expands when it gets hot and creates higher pressure. When it gets cold, air contracts and creates ___(A)___ pressure. When the flame burnt out, the air inside the glass ②heated up. As the air ③cooled down, the air pressure ④dropped. So the air ⑤outside the glass was at a higher pressure. It pushed the water into the glass.

**04** 다음 중 빈칸 (A)에 들어갈 말로 가장 적절한 것은?

① higher    ② the same    ③ lower
④ no    ⑤ strong

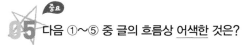

**05** 다음 ①~⑤ 중 글의 흐름상 어색한 것은?

①        ②        ③        ④        ⑤

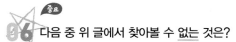

**06** 다음 중 위 글에서 찾아볼 수 없는 것은?

① a boy who is showing a magic
② a girl watching a magic show
③ a dish which has water in it
④ a candle covered with a towel
⑤ water pushed into the glass from outside of the dish

서답형

**07** What happened when Kevin covered the candle with a glass? Answer in English with a full sentence.

➡ _____

**08** 다음 중 위 글을 읽고 답할 수 있는 것은?

① How much water is there in the dish?
② What does Ken want to show?
③ How did Ken learn the magic?
④ Where did Ken show the magic?
⑤ When did Ken show the magic?

**09** 위 글의 내용에 맞게 빈칸에 알맞은 말을 쓰시오.

> Pressure _____ causes the water to move into the glass.

[10~15] 다음 글을 읽고 물음에 답하시오.

> Ken: Now, I'm going to fill one of these cups with water. I will move them around to confuse you. Jina, which cup has the water in it?
>
> Jina: That's easy! It's the middle one.
>
> Ken: Okay, let's check. See? No water.
>
> Jina: Show me ___(A)___ cups.
>
> Ken: See? There's no water.
>
> Jina: Wow! How come the water disappeared?
>
> Ken: ① Before the trick, I put a special material into one of the cups. ② The material absorbed the water and turned it into jelly. ③ If you want to try this trick, it's necessary to use cups that you can't see through. ④
>
> Jina: ⑤ Thank you for your great performance. It was really amazing!

**10** 다음 중 빈칸 (A)에 들어갈 말로 가장 적절한 것은?

① the others        ② another
③ other             ④ the other
⑤ others

**11** 다음 ①~⑤ 중 주어진 문장이 들어가기에 가장 적절한 곳은?

> Then the jelly stuck to the bottom.

①        ②        ③        ④        ⑤

**12** 다음과 같이 풀이되는 단어를 위 글에서 찾아 쓰시오.

> to take in something in a natural or gradual way

➡ _____

**13** What did Ken do after he filled one of cups with water? Answer in English with four words.

➡ _____

**14** According to Ken, what is necessary if we want to try the trick?

➡ _____
_____

**15** 다음 중 위 글의 내용을 바르게 이해한 사람은?

① Teo: If there is no mysterious power, we can't perform the magic.
② Jenny: I will need only two cups to try the magic.
③ Chris: Ken made the water disappear by drinking it when no one saw him.
④ Paul: To try the magic, I will buy the special material which can take in water and turn it into jelly.
⑤ Nick: I need to buy a special material and some glasses which people can see through.

**[16~18]** 다음 글을 읽고 물음에 답하시오.

Jina: Welcome to the Super Science Magic Show! (A)It's always exciting to see magic tricks. And it's more exciting to find out the secrets behind (B)them. Some people think the secret of magic is science. Today, Ken, a member of the School Magic Club, will use science to perform his tricks. Which tricks will he show us? I can't wait to see them.

**16** 다음 중 밑줄 친 (A)와 쓰임이 같은 것은?

① It is rainy and windy.

② It is not what I said.

③ It is clear that you can't drive.

④ It is dark outside.

⑤ It is flowing under the bridge.

**17** 다음 밑줄 친 (B)가 가리키는 것을 위 글에서 찾아 쓰시오.

➡ _____

**18** 다음 중 위 글에 이어질 내용으로 가장 적절한 것은?

① Ken의 자기소개

② Ken의 과학을 이용한 발명품

③ Jina의 과학 동아리 소개

④ Ken의 과학을 이용한 마술 쇼

⑤ 마술에 숨겨진 비밀

**[19~23]** 다음 글을 읽고 물음에 답하시오.

Jina: Hello, everyone. Today, I'm going to show you ①amazing something.
(A) Next, I'll light the candle and cover it with a glass. "Abracadabra!"
(B) Now, I'll put a candle ②in the middle of the dish.
(C) Here's a dish with water in it.

Jina: Look at the water! _____ⓐ_____

Ken: Air expands when it gets hot and creates higher pressure. When it ③gets cold, air contracts and creates lower pressure. When the flame ④burnt out, the air inside the glass cooled down. As the air cooled down, the air pressure dropped. So the air outside the glass was at a higher pressure. It pushed the water ⑤into the glass.

**19** 다음 중 빈칸 ⓐ에 들어갈 말로 가장 적절한 것은?

① Why did you cover it with a glass?

② How come you pour more water?

③ How come there is no water?

④ Why did you light the candle?

⑤ How come it rose into the glass?

**20** 자연스러운 글이 되도록 (A)~(C)를 바르게 배열한 것은?

① (A) – (C) – (B)  ② (B) – (A) – (C)

③ (B) – (C) – (A)  ④ (C) – (B) – (A)

⑤ (C) – (A) – (B)

서답형

**21** According to the passage, which side of the air is at a higher pressure while the candle is still burning? Answer in English with a full sentence.

➡ _____

**22** 다음 ①~⑤ 중 어법상 바르지 않은 것은?

①       ②       ③       ④       ⑤

서답형

**23** 주어진 단어를 활용하여 Ken의 마술 쇼 제목을 쓰시오.

> The _____ Water (amaze, rise)

➡ _____

[24~27] 다음 글을 읽고 물음에 답하시오.

> **Ken:** Now, I'm going to fill one of these cups with water. I will move them around to confuse you. Jina, which cup has the water in it?
>
> **Jina:** That's easy! It's the middle one.
>
> **Ken:** Okay, let's check. See? No water.
>
> **Jina:** Show me the other cups.
>
> **Ken:** See? There's no water.
>
> **Jina:** Wow! (A)어째서 물이 사라진 거죠?
>
> **Ken:** Before the trick, I put (B)<u>a special material</u> into one of the cups. The material absorbed the water and turned it into jelly. Then the jelly stuck to the bottom. If you want to try this trick, it's necessary to use cups (C)<u>that</u> you can't see through.
>
> **Jina:** Thank you for your great performance. It was really amazing!

서답형

**24** 주어진 단어를 활용하여 밑줄 친 우리말 (A)를 영어로 쓰시오.

> (how)

➡ _____

**25** 다음 중 밑줄 친 (B)에 관한 설명으로 옳은 것은?

① Ken put it into one of the cups after the show.

② It can't take in water.

③ It turns water into jelly after absorbing water.

④ It is easy to remove it from the cup.

⑤ You should put it into all of the cups when trying the magic.

**26** 다음 중 밑줄 친 (C)와 쓰임이 같은 것은?

① I thought <u>that</u> we were lost.

② It was surprising <u>that</u> he accepted their apology.

③ The fact <u>that</u> he spread the news shocked everyone.

④ Did he say <u>that</u> he didn't serve the table?

⑤ The boy <u>that</u> you shook hands with is my cousin, Alan.

서답형

**27** Write the reason why Ken moved around the cups after filling one of them with water. Answer in English with a full sentence.

➡ _____

[28~29] 다음 글을 읽고 물음에 답하시오.

> USA – The moving rocks in Death Valley
>
> How come the rocks move ___(A)___ their own? They weigh up to 300 kilograms each. Some scientists have watched their movements closely for a long time. Now we know that ice and wind move the rocks.

중요

**28** 다음 중 빈칸 (A)에 들어갈 말로 가장 적절한 것은?

① in     ② about     ③ at

④ on     ⑤ out

서답형

**29** 위 글의 내용에 맞게 빈칸에 알맞은 말을 쓰시오.

> According to the research of the scientists, _____ make the rocks look like they move by themselves.

[01~03] 다음 글을 읽고 물음에 답하시오.

Jina: Welcome to the Super Science Magic Show! (A)It's always exciting to see magic tricks. And it's more exciting to find out the secrets behind them. Some people think the secret of magic is science. Today, Ken, a member of the School Magic Club, will use science to perform his tricks. Which tricks will he show us? I can't wait to see them.

**01** According to Jina, what is more exciting about magic tricks? Answer in English with a full sentence.

➡ _____

_____

**02** What will Ken perform? Answer in English with seven words.

➡ _____

**03** 밑줄 친 (A)가 의미하는 것을 위 글에서 찾아 쓰시오.

➡ _____

[04~08] 다음 글을 읽고 물음에 답하시오.

Ken: Hello, everyone. Today, I'm going to show you something amazing. Here's a dish with water in it. Now, I'll put a candle in the middle of the dish. Next, I'll light the candle and cover it with a glass. "Abracadabra!"

Jina: Look at the water! ____(A)____ it rose into the glass?

Ken: Air expands when it gets hot and creates higher pressure. When it gets cold, air contracts and creates lower pressure.

When the flame burnt out, the air inside the glass cooled down. As the air cooled down, the air pressure dropped. So the air outside the glass was at a higher pressure. It pushed the water into the glass.

**04** 빈칸 (A)에 알맞은 말을 쓰시오.

➡ _____

**05** Where did Ken put the candle? Answer in English with a full sentence.

➡ _____

**06** When air gets hot, what happens? Answer in English with a full sentence.

➡ _____

**07** 위 글의 내용에 맞게 빈칸에 알맞은 말을 쓰시오.

> When air gets cold, it becomes smaller in size and creates _____ _____.

**08** 위 글의 내용에 맞게 빈칸에 알맞은 말을 쓰시오.

> _____ Water Trick
> When the flame _____ _____, the air inside the glass _____ down and the air pressure _____. The _____ air pressure _____ the glass _____ the water into the glass.

[09~12] 다음 글을 읽고 물음에 답하시오.

Ken: Now, I'm going to fill one of these cups with water. I will move them around to confuse you. Jina, which cup has the water in it?

Jina: That's easy! It's the middle one.

Ken: Okay, let's check. See? No water.

Jina: Show me the other cups.

Ken: See? There's no water.

Jina: Wow! How come the water disappeared?

Ken: Before the trick, I put a special material into one of the cups. The material absorbed the water and turned it into jelly. Then the jelly stuck to the bottom. If you want to try this trick, (A)to use cups that you can't see through is necessary.

Jina: Thank you for your great performance. (B)It was really amazing!

**09** 위 글의 내용에 맞게 다음 빈칸에 알맞은 말을 쓰시오.

> Jina thought that the cup _____ _____
> _____ _____ _____ is the
> middle one.

**10** What happens when the special material turns water into jelly? Answer in English and use the phrase 'of the cup.'

➡ _____

**11** 밑줄 친 (A)와 같은 의미의 문장을 쓰시오.

➡ _____

**12** 밑줄 친 (B)가 가리키는 것을 위 글에서 찾아 쓰시오.

➡ _____

[13~15] 다음 글을 읽고 물음에 답하시오.

A Dancing Coin

Can a coin dance? Let's test it. You need a coin and a bottle. Before you start, (A)병을 차갑게 하는 것이 중요합니다.(it)

Q: How do you do it?

A: First, put a coin on the mouth of the bottle. Then, hold the bottle in your hands for a while.

Q: What happens?

A: The coin moves up and down

Q: How come the coin moves?

A: Your hands warm the cold air inside the bottle. As the air gets warm, it expands. The expanding air tries to escape from the bottle.

**13** What do we need to prepare to try the trick? Answer in English with a full sentence.

➡ _____

**14** 주어진 단어를 활용하여 밑줄 친 우리말 (A)를 영어로 쓰시오.

➡ _____

**15** 다음은 위 글을 요약한 것이다. 글의 내용과 일치하지 <u>않는</u> 것을 두 개 찾아 바르게 고쳐 쓰시오.

> There is a simple trick you can do if you have a coin and a bottle. First, prepare a cool bottle. Second, put a coin on the bottom of the bottle. Third, hold the bottle with your hands for some time. Then, the coin will spin.

➡ _____

➡ _____

## Real Life Communication B

**A:** Which class do you want to sign up for?

**B:** I want to take the badminton class. I like playing badminton. How about
you?
= What about you?

**A:** I want to take the computer class. I can't wait to make a computer program
there.
= look forward to making

= at the computer class

**B:** That sounds cool!

구문해설 • **sign up for**: ~을 신청하다, 등록하다

해석

A: 무슨 수업을 등록하고 싶니?
B: 난 배드민턴 수업을 듣고 싶어. 나는 배드민턴 치는 것을 좋아하거든. 너는?
A: 난 컴퓨터 수업을 듣고 싶어. 나는 빨리 거기에서 컴퓨터 프로그램을 만들고 싶어.
B: 멋진 것 같다!

## Culture & Life

### North Atlantic Ocean – The Bermuda Triangle

A number of airplanes and ships have disappeared in the Bermuda Triangle.
a number of+복수명사                          자동사 (수동태 불가)
How come? It's still a mystery.
= Why?

구문해설 • **a number of**: 많은 • **disappear**: 사라지다 • **still**: 여전히

북대서양 – 버뮤다 삼각 지대
많은 비행기와 선박이 버뮤다 삼각 지대에서 사라졌다. 이유가 무엇일까? 그것은 여전히 미스터리이다.

## Culture & Life

### Egypt – The pyramids

Some of the rocks that were used to build the pyramids weigh about 70 tons.
주격 관계대명사 be used to V: V 하는 데 사용되다                  대략(전치사)
How was it possible to move such heavy rocks back then? It's still a mystery.
가주어        진주어 to부정사

구문해설 • **rock**: 바위 • **build**: 짓다 • **weigh**: 무게가 나가다 • **possible**: 가능한

이집트 – 피라미드
피라미드를 만드는 데 사용된 몇몇 바위들은 무게가 70톤 정도인 것들이 있다. 어떻게 그 시대에 그렇게 무거운 바위를 옮기는 것이 가능했을까? 그것은 여전히 미스터리이다.

**Words & Expressions**

**01** 다음 영영풀이가 가리키는 것을 고르시오.

> having the power to make impossible things happen

① necessary    ② magic
③ instead    ④ dry
⑤ safe

**02** 다음 중 밑줄 친 부분의 뜻풀이가 바르지 않은 것은?

① Would you push the window up? 밀다
② There is a huge difference between them. 차이
③ Mix some water with the flour. 섞다
④ Don't forget to put the ice cream back in the freezer. 냉동실
⑤ The boat was beginning to sink fast. 세면대

**03** 다음 우리말에 맞게 빈칸에 알맞은 말을 쓰시오.

(1) 타 버리고 꽃으로 변해라!
  ➡ Burn out and _____ _____ a flower!

(2) 유리컵 속의 공기는 차가워졌다.
  ➡ The air inside the glass _____ _____.

(3) 어째서 Ken은 당신이 속을 들여다 볼 수 없는 컵을 사용했는가?
  ➡ How come Ken used cups that you can't _____ _____.

(4) 그 물질은 물을 흡수하고 그것을 젤리로 변화시켰다.
  ➡ The material absorbed the water and _____ it _____ jelly.

**04** 다음 주어진 문장의 밑줄 친 sink와 다른 의미로 쓰인 것은?

> Don't leave your dirty plates in the sink.

① He is washing cups in the sink.
② The boat began to sink like a stone.
③ The sink is filled with water.
④ The sponge absorbed water from the sink.
⑤ The sink should be fixed to be used again.

**05** 다음 문장에 공통으로 들어갈 말을 고르시오.

> • Would you _____ the milk with the flour?
> • The cook is adding something to the _____.
> • Water and oil do not _____.

① practice    ② mix    ③ move
④ contract    ⑤ absorb

**06** 우리말과 일치하도록 주어진 어구를 모두 배열하여 영작하시오.

(1) 어느 불꽃이 먼저 꺼질까요?
  (out / first / which / will / flame / burn)
  ➡ _____

(2) 나의 딸이 케이크 위에 촛불을 불었다.
  (her / on / cake / my / blew / daughter / the candles / out)
  ➡ _____

(3) 물은 기온의 변화에 따라 팽창하고 수축한다.
  (and / with / changes / temperature / in / expands / water / contracts)
  ➡ _____
  _____

Conversation

**07** 다음 짝지어진 대화가 <u>어색한</u> 것은?

① A: Which trick do you want to learn?

B: The ballon trick looks interesting. I want to learn how to move a can without touching it.

② A: Look at that girl. She's driving a robot.

B: That looks really fun. I can't wait to try it.

③ A: Which eggs are fresh, and which ones are not?

B: I can't wait to tell the difference.

④ A: Which program do you want to do at the science museum, Mira?

B: I want to make lightning.

⑤ A: Which movie do you want to see?

B: I want to see a 4D movie.

**[08~10]** 다음 대화를 읽고 물음에 답하시오.

King Sejong: It ⓐ<u>hasn't rained</u> for a long time.

Jang Yeongsil: Yes. The dry season is lasting too long. The farmers are very worried.

King Sejong: We should do something ⓑ<u>to help</u> them.

Jang Yeongsil: How about making a special clock?

King Sejong: A clock? How will that help?

Jang Yeongsil: The clock will show the time and the seasons. We can use it ⓒ <u>to prepare</u> for the dry season.

King Sejong: That ⓓ<u>sound</u> like a good idea. But who's going to make it?

Jang Yeongsil: I'll give it a try. I know a lot about time and the seasons.

King Sejong: Okay, I can't wait ⓔ<u>to see</u> your clock.

**08** 위 대화의 밑줄 친 ⓐ~ⓔ 중 어법상 어색한 것을 찾아 바르게 고치시오.

➡ _____

**09** 위 대화에서 나타난 세종대왕의 기분 변화로 적절한 것은?

① worried → disappointed

② worried → pleased

③ disappointed → nervous

④ disappointed → worried

⑤ pleased → worried

**10** 위 대화의 내용과 일치하지 <u>않는</u> 것은?

① 비가 오랫동안 내리지 않았다.

② 건기가 너무 오래 계속 되고 있어 농부들이 매우 걱정하고 있다.

③ 장영실은 농부들을 돕기 위해 특별한 시계를 만들 것을 제안하였다.

④ 장영실은 시간과 계절에 대해 많이 알고 있다.

⑤ 장영실은 비가 내리게 하기 위해 시계를 만들고자 한다.

**[11~12]** 다음 대화를 읽고 물음에 답하시오.

Brian: Yujin, why did you put the eggs in water?

Yujin: I'm picking out the bad eggs.

Brian: Which eggs are fresh, and which ones are not?

Yujin: Eggs that sink in water are fresh. When eggs float in water, they're not fresh. You shouldn't eat them.

Brian: That's interesting. Why do the bad eggs float?

Yujin: Because they have gas inside. The gas acts like the air in a balloon.

Brian: Oh, I see.

**11** 위 대화에서 다음의 영영풀이가 가리키는 것을 찾아 쓰시오.

> to go down below the surface of water

➡ _____

**12** 위 대화를 읽고 대답할 수 <u>없는</u> 것은?

① What is Yujin doing with the eggs?
② How can Yujin tell the fresh eggs from the bad ones?
③ What do the bad eggs have inside?
④ What does the gas act like?
⑤ What is Yujin going to do with a balloon?

**13** 〈보기〉에 주어진 단어를 다음 글의 빈칸에 알맞게 쓰시오.

┌─── 보기 ───┐
strawberry / try / put / mix / cut / flavor
└────────┘

**Jane:** Today we'll make ice cream. Which (A)_____ do you want to make? How about (B)_____ ? First, (C)_____ two cups of milk, two cups of heavy cream, and half a cup of sugar. Next, (D)_____ five strawberries into small pieces. Then, mix everything together and (E)_____ it in the freezer. That's it. It's easy to make, isn't it? Why don't you (F)_____ making it at home?

**14** 다음 우리말을 영어로 바르게 옮긴 것은?

> 네가 우리를 위해 나서 준 것은 정말 용감했어.

① It was brave you to step forward for us.
② It was brave for you to step forward for you.
③ It was brave of you step forward for us.
④ It was brave of you to step forward for us.
⑤ It was brave with you to step forward for us.

**15** 다음 빈칸에 들어갈 말로 적절하지 <u>않은</u> 것은?

> It is _____ for me to share my room with her.

① difficult   ② wise   ③ easy
④ hard   ⑤ necessary

**16** 다음 중 어법상 바르지 <u>않은</u> 것은?

① It is important to listen to others.
② It is foolish of you to behave like that.
③ How come you didn't take the umbrella?
④ Is it possible of her to stop biting her nail?
⑤ To see is to believe.

**17** 다음 중 밑줄 친 부분의 쓰임이 <u>다른</u> 하나는?

① It is okay for you <u>to wear</u> my clothes.
② <u>To keep</u> this place safe is important.
③ The bird is building a nest <u>to lay</u> eggs.
④ It is good <u>to go</u> out with you tonight.
⑤ <u>To meet</u> him in person is amazing.

**18** 주어진 단어를 활용하여 다음 우리말을 영어로 쓰시오.

> 그녀가 그 상자들을 옮기는 것은 쉽지 않아요.
> (it / move)

➡ _____

**19** 다음 빈칸에 들어갈 말이 바르게 짝지어진 것은?

> _____ is boring _____ he keeps
> saying the same thing over and over.

① That – that　　② It – to
③ It – that　　④ To – to
⑤ That – to

**20** 다음 중 빈칸에 들어갈 말이 <u>다른</u> 하나는?

① _____ she told you to go?
② _____ they didn't make it?
③ _____ he didn't want to see us?
④ _____ was there no one in the room?
⑤ _____ you didn't have your dinner?

**21** 다음 빈칸에 들어갈 말로 가장 적절한 것은?

> 왜 그는 매번 우리를 비난하는 거야?
> ➡ _____ he blames us every time?

① Why　　② What　　③ When
④ Who　　⑤ How come

**22** 다음 중 어법상 옳은 문장은?

① That is necessary to tell the truth.
② It is kind for her to read a book to us.
③ Why do you look unsatisfied?
④ It is fun play tennis with friends.
⑤ How come did he drink the coffee?

**23** 주어진 단어를 활용하여 다음 문장과 같은 의미의 문장을 쓰시오.

> Why did she make an appointment?
> (come)

➡ _____

**24** 다음 빈칸에 알맞은 말을 쓰시오.

> Was it strange that he said so?
> ➡ Was it strange _____ _____ to
> say so?

---

**Reading**

**[25~27]** 다음 글을 읽고 물음에 답하시오.

Ken: Hello, everyone. Today, I'm going to show you something amazing. Here's a dish with water in it. Now, I'll put a candle in the middle of the dish. Next, I'll (A)light the candle and cover it with a glass. "Abracadabra!"

Jina: Look at the water! How come it rose into the glass?

**25** 다음 중 밑줄 친 (A)와 같은 의미로 쓰인 것은?

① This is a room with natural <u>light</u>.
② Did you turn the <u>light</u> on?
③ Julia has <u>light</u> blue eyes.
④ I need to buy <u>light</u> summer clothes.
⑤ She wanted to <u>light</u> a cooking stove.

**26** 위 글에 이어질 내용으로 가장 적절한 것은?

① the reason why Ken likes to do magic
② the time when Ken first started to do magic
③ the next magic that Ken prepared
④ the reason why the water rose into the glass
⑤ how Ken made the water disappear

**27** 위 마술의 원리를 바르게 배열하시오.

> Air expands when it gets hot and creates higher pressure. And when it gets cold, air contracts and creates lower pressure.
> ⓐ So the air outside the glass was at a higher pressure.
> ⓑ It pushed the water into the glass.
> ⓒ As the air cooled down, the air pressure dropped.
> ⓓ When the flame burnt out, the air inside the glass cooled down.

➡ _____

[28~30] 다음 글을 읽고 물음에 답하시오.

Ken: Air expands when it gets hot and creates ①<u>higher</u> pressure. When it gets cold, air ②<u>contracts</u> and creates lower pressure. When the flame burnt out, the air inside the glass cooled down. As the air ③<u>cooled down</u>, the air pressure ④<u>dropped</u>. So the air outside the glass was at a higher pressure. (A)It ⑤<u>pulled</u> the water into the glass.

**28** 다음 밑줄 친 (A)가 가리키는 말을 위 글에서 찾아 쓰시오.

➡ _____

**29** 위 글의 ①~⑤ 중 글의 흐름상 어색한 것은?

①     ②     ③     ④     ⑤

**30** 다음과 같이 풀이할 수 있는 말을 위 글에서 찾아 쓰시오.

> to increase in size, range, or amount

➡ _____

[31~32] 다음 대화를 읽고 물음에 답하시오.

> Ken: Now, I'm going to fill one of these cups _____(A)_____. I will move them around to confuse you. Jina, which cup has the water in it?
> Jina: That's easy! It's the middle one.
> Ken: Okay, let's check. See? No water.
> Jina: Show me the other cups.
> Ken: See? There's no water.
> Jina: Wow! How come the water disappeared?

**31** 다음 중 빈칸 (A)에 들어갈 말로 가장 적절한 것은?

① with sand     ② with water
③ with oil     ④ with another cup
⑤ with balls

**32** 다음 중 위 대화의 제목으로 가장 적절한 것은?

① The Magic of a Disappearing Cup
② The Amazing Science Experiment
③ The Secret of the Special Material
④ The Man Who Disappeared
⑤ The Secret of the Disappearing Water

**[01~02]** 다음 글을 읽고 물음에 답하시오.

> Jane: Today we'll make ice cream. (A)여러분은 어떤 맛을 만들고 싶은가요? How about strawberry? First, mix two cups of milk, two cups of heavy cream, and half a cup of sugar. Next, cut five strawberries into small pieces. Then, mix everything together and put it in the freezer. That's it. It's easy to make, isn't it? Why don't you try making it at home?

출제율 90%

**01** 위 글의 밑줄 친 (A)의 우리말을 주어진 단어를 이용하여 영작하시오. (which, flavor, make)

➡ _____

출제율 85%

**02** 위 글에서 다음 영영풀이가 나타내는 말을 찾아 쓰시오.

> to combine two or more substances so that they become a single substance

➡ _____

**[03~04]** 다음 대화를 읽고 물음에 답하시오.

> Brian: Yujin, why did you put the eggs in water?
> Yujin: (A) I'm picking out the bad eggs.
> Brian: (B) Which eggs are fresh, and which ones are not?
> Yujin: (C) When eggs float in water, they're not fresh. You shouldn't eat them.
> Brian: (D) That's interesting. Why do the bad eggs float?
> Yujin: (E) Because they have gas inside. The gas acts like the air in a balloon.
> Brian: Oh, I see.

출제율 100%

**03** 위 대화의 (A)~(E) 중 주어진 문장이 들어가기에 적절한 곳은?

> Eggs that sink in water are fresh.

① (A)  ② (B)  ③ (C)  ④ (D)  ⑤ (E)

출제율 85%

**04** 위 대화의 내용과 일치하도록 빈칸에 알맞은 말을 쓰시오.

> When eggs _____ in water, they're fresh. On the other hand, the eggs that _____ in water are not fresh. Bad eggs have _____ inside. It acts like the _____ in a balloon.

**[05~06]** 다음 대화를 읽고 물음에 답하시오.

> Minsu: What are you reading, Jiwon?
> Jiwon: I'm reading a book ⓐabout magic and science.
> Minsu: That sounds ⓑinteresting.
> Jiwon: Yes. This book introduces 100 magic tricks that ⓒuses science. I've ⓓlearned about half of them.
> Minsu: That's cool. Can you show me some of the tricks?
> Jiwon: Sure. I can show you a balloon trick now.
> Minsu: Great! I can't wait ⓔto see it.

출제율 90%

**05** 위 대화의 밑줄 친 ⓐ~ⓔ 중 어법상 어색한 것을 찾아 바르게 고치시오.

➡ _____

출제율 95%

**06** 위 대화를 읽고 대답할 수 없는 것은?

① What is Jiwon reading?
② What does the book introduce?
③ How many tricks has Jiwon learned from the book?
④ Which trick can Jiwon show to Minsu?
⑤ How long has Jiwon practiced a balloon trick?

**[07~08]** 다음 대화를 읽고 물음에 답하시오.

Brian: Mina, will you join our tennis club?

Mina: It sounds interesting, but I signed up for a special class this fall.

Brian: Which class did you sign up for?

Mina: I signed up for a magic class. I can't wait to learn new magic tricks there.

Brian: That sounds cool! Have you learned magic tricks before?

Mina: Yes, I learned some before, but I need more practice.

Brian: I hope I can see your magic tricks some day.

**07** 출제율 90%

Which class did Mina sign up for this fall?

➡ _____

**08** 출제율 95%

What is Mina looking forward to?

➡ _____

**[09~10]** 다음 대화를 읽고 물음에 답하시오.

Jaemin: Ms. Jeong, does a glass of water weigh more when there's a fish in it?

Ms. Jeong: (A) Yes, it does. We can test it now.

Jaemin: (B) But how? We don't have a fish.

Ms. Jeong: (C) We can use a finger instead of a fish.

Jaemin: (D) How will that work?

Ms. Jeong: (E) Then I will put my finger in the water and weigh it to compare.

Jaemin: Oh, (F)I can't wait to see the difference.
(to, looking)

**09** 출제율 100%

위 대화의 (A)~(E) 중 주어진 문장이 들어가기에 적절한 곳은?

I'll weigh a glass of water first.

① (A)　② (B)　③ (C)　④ (D)　⑤ (E)

**10** 출제율 85%

위 대화의 밑줄 친 (F)와 의미가 같도록 주어진 단어들을 사용하여 다시 쓰시오.

➡ _____

**11** 출제율 90%

다음 빈칸에 들어갈 말로 가장 적절한 것은?

How come _____ the flower?

① did she send　② does he cut

③ she brought　④ did you bring

⑤ did I send

**12** 출제율 100%

다음 빈칸에 들어갈 말이 나머지와 다른 하나는?

① It is difficult _____ us to know who wrote the letter.

② Is it hard _____ you to focus on what you are doing?

③ It is necessary _____ him to drink eight glasses of water every day.

④ It is careful _____ her to bring her purse all the time.

⑤ Is it important _____ them to be on time here?

**13** 출제율 80%

다음 우리말을 영어로 옮길 때 빈칸에 알맞은 말을 쓰시오.

네가 그러한 결정을 내린 것은 정말 현명했어.

➡ _____ _____ _____ _____

_____ make such a decision.

**14** 다음 중 어법상 옳은 문장은?

① Is it possible to finding something meaningful in your life?
② How come is she complaining about it?
③ It is rude of you to not follow the advice.
④ Why he is sitting over there?
⑤ It is dangerous for us to swim in the river.

**15** 다음 중 어법상 옳은 것끼리 바르게 짝지은 것은?

(A) [That / It] is impossible to meet Ann on Sunday afternoon.
(B) It is important [to / that] he takes part in the race.
(C) [Why / How come] you lost the cap?

① That – to – Why
② That – that – How come
③ That – to – How come
④ It – that – How come
⑤ It – to – Why

**16** 주어진 어구를 활용하여 다음 우리말을 영어로 쓰시오.

그가 그 대회에서 우승했다는 것은 놀랍다.
(surprising / the competition / that / it)

➡ _____

**17** 일곱 개의 단어를 사용하여 다음 문장과 같은 의미의 문장을 쓰시오.

Why are you home so early?

➡ _____

**[18~21]** 다음 글을 읽고 물음에 답하시오.

Ken: Now, I'm going to fill one of these cups with water. I will move them around (A) to confuse you. Jina, which cup has the water in it?
Jina: That's easy! It's the middle one.
Ken: Okay, let's check. See? No water.
Jina: Show me the other cups.
Ken: See? There's no water.
Jina: Wow! How come the water disappeared?
Ken: Before the trick, I put a special material into one of the cups. The material absorbed the water and turned it into jelly. Then the jelly stuck to the bottom. If you want to try this trick, (B)it's necessary to use cups that you can't see through.
Jina: Thank you for your great performance. It was really amazing!

**18** 다음 중 밑줄 친 (A)와 쓰임이 같은 것은?

① I want you to tidy your room.
② He tried hard to succeed.
③ Is there any chance to win the race?
④ It is nice to hear it from you.
⑤ She planned to open a new office.

**19** 다음 중 위 글의 내용과 일치하는 것은?

① Ken prepared two cups.
② Jina thought it was difficult to find which cup had the water in it.
③ Ken moved around the cups to make Jina confused.
④ Jina didn't want to see if the other cups had the water in it.
⑤ Jina wasn't interested in the reason why the water disappeared.

**출제율 90%**

**20** Ken이 밑줄 친 (B)와 같이 말한 이유를 우리말로 쓰시오.

➡ _____

**출제율 95%**

**21** 다음 중 Ken이 마술을 보여 주기 위하여 가장 먼저 한 일은?

① moving around the cups to confuse people

② pouring water into one of the cups

③ putting a special material into one of the cups

④ buying some jelly to treat people

⑤ preparing a cup which has a hole

**[22~25]** 다음 글을 읽고 물음에 답하시오.

**A Dancing Coin**

Can a coin dance? Let's test it. You need a coin and a bottle. Before you start, it is important to cool the bottle.

Q: _____ ⓐ _____

A: First, put a coin on the mouth of the bottle. Then, hold the bottle in your hands for a while.

Q: _____ ⓑ _____

A: The coin moves up and down.

Q: _____ ⓒ _____

A: Your hands warm the cold air inside the bottle. As the air gets warm, it expands. The (A)_____ air tries to escape from the bottle.

**출제율 95%**

**22** 다음 빈칸 ⓐ~ⓒ에 주어진 문장을 내용에 맞게 쓰시오.

- What happens?
- How come the coin moves?
- How do you do it?

ⓐ _____

ⓑ _____

ⓒ _____

**출제율 90%**

**23** 위 글의 단어를 활용하여 빈칸 (A)에 알맞은 말을 쓰시오.

➡ _____

**출제율 100%**

**24** What is important to do before we do the magic?

① We should prepare an empty bottle.

② We need to prepare as many coins as possible.

③ Cooling the bottle is important.

④ It is important to keep the bottle open.

⑤ We should prepare a clean bottle.

**출제율 85%**

**25** 글의 내용에 맞게 빈칸에 알맞은 말을 쓰시오.

Because of the air _____ _____ _____ _____ _____, the coin on the mouth of the bottle moves up and down.

[01~03] 다음 대화를 읽고 물음에 답하시오.

Jang Yeongsil: Yes. The dry season is lasting too long. The farmers are very worried.

King Sejong: We should do something to help them.

Jang Yeongsil: How about making a special clock?

King Sejong: A clock? How will that help?

Jang Yeongsil: The clock will show the time and the seasons. We can use it to prepare for the dry season.

King Sejong: That sounds like a good idea. But who's going to make it?

Jang Yeongsil: I'll give it a try. I know a lot about time and the seasons.

King Sejong: Okay, I can't wait to see your clock.

**01** What's the problem with King Sejong and Jang Yeongsil?

➡ _____

**02**  What does Jang Yeongsil suggest doing?

➡ _____

**03** Why does Jang Yeongsil think the clock will help the farmers?

➡ _____

_____

**04** 주어진 어구를 바르게 배열하여 다음 우리말을 영어로 쓰시오. 두 개의 단어를 추가하시오.

> 그녀의 허락 없이 그녀의 사진을 찍다니 그는 무례해.
>
> (her permission / it / without / rude / her / is / him / take / of / pictures)

➡ _____

_____

**05**  다음 빈칸에 알맞은 말을 쓰시오.

> It is amazing that he exercises regularly.
> = It is amazing _____ _____ _____ exercise regularly.

**06** 다음 대화의 빈칸에 들어갈 말을 일곱 단어로 쓰시오.

> A: _____
> B: I couldn't catch the bus because he woke up late.

**07** 다음 주어진 문장과 같은 의미의 문장을 쓰시오.

> To keep a diary is important.
> = _____ a diary.

**08** 주어진 단어를 활용하여 다음 우리말을 영어로 쓰시오.

> 도대체 왜 그들은 피곤한 거야? (how)

➡ _____

Jina: Wow! (A)How come the water disappeared?

Ken: Before the trick, I put a special material into one of the cups. The material absorbed the water and turned it into jelly. Then the jelly stuck to the bottom. If you want to try this trick, it's necessary to use cups that you can't see through.

Jina: Thank you for your great performance. It was really amazing!

**09** What did Ken put into one of the cups? Answer in English with a full sentence.

➡ _____

**10** How come the water in the cup turned into jelly? Answer in English with a full sentence.

➡ _____
   _____

**11** 주어진 단어를 활용하여 문장 (A)와 같은 의미의 문장을 쓰시오.

| (why) |
| --- |

➡ _____

A Dancing Coin

  Can a coin dance? Let's test it. You need a coin and a bottle. Before you start, it is important to cool the bottle.

Q: How do you do it?

A: First, put a coin on the mouth of the bottle. Then, hold the bottle in your hands for a while.

Q: What happens?

A: The coin moves up and down.

Q: How come the coin moves?

A: Your hands ___(A)___ the cold air inside the bottle. As the air ___(B)___ warm, it ___(C)___. The expanding air tries to ___(D)___ from the bottle.

**12** 주어진 단어를 내용에 맞게 빈칸 (A)~(D)에 쓰시오. 필요하다면 어형을 바꾸시오.

| escape / warm / expand / get |
| --- |

(A) _____    (B) _____
(C) _____    (D) _____

**13** 위 마술의 순서를 바르게 배열하시오.

| ⓐ Hold the bottle in your hands. |
| --- |
| ⓑ Cool a bottle. |
| ⓒ After a while, the coin will move. |
| ⓓ Put a coin on the mouth of the bottle. |

➡ _____

**01** 다음 대화의 내용과 일치하도록 빈칸을 완성하시오.

> King Sejong: It hasn't rained for a long time.
>
> Jang Yeongsil: Yes. The dry season is lasting too long. The farmers are very worried.
>
> King Sejong: We should do something to help them.
>
> Jang Yeongsil: How about making a special clock?
>
> King Sejong: A clock? How will that help?
>
> Jang Yeongsil: The clock will show the time and the seasons. We can use it to prepare for the dry season.
>
> King Sejong: That sounds like a good idea. But who's going to make it?
>
> Jang Yeongsil: I'll give it a try. I know a lot about time and the seasons.
>
> King Sejong: Okay, I can't wait to see your clock.

> King Sejong was worried about farmers because (A)_____ was lasting too long. When he looked for the way to help them, Jang Yeonsil suggested making (B)_____. King Sejong wondered how that clock could help farmers. Jang Yeonsil explained that the clock would show (C)_____, so it could be used (D)_____. Fortunately, Jang Yeongsli knew a lot about (E)_____, so he tried to invent it.

**02** 가주어 it과 주어진 to부정사구를 활용하여 여러 가지 문장을 쓰시오.

> to make many friends / to love your pet / to save your allowance / to think others first

(1) _____

(2) _____

(3) _____

(4) _____

## 단원별 모의고사

**01** 다음 영영풀이가 가리키는 것을 고르시오.

> a device or room for freezing food or keeping it frozen

① coin  ② balloon
③ freezer  ④ candle
⑤ pressure

**02** 다음 우리말에 맞게 빈칸에 알맞은 말을 쓰시오.

(1) 가스는 풍선 안의 공기처럼 작용한다.
➡ The gas acts like the air in a _____.

(2) 나는 접시 한 가운데에 양초를 놓을 것이다.
➡ I'll put a _____ in the middle of the dish.

(3) 나는 비교하기 위해서 물속에 내 손가락을 넣을 것이다.
➡ I will put my finger in the water to _____.

**03** 다음 문장의 빈칸에 들어갈 말을 〈보기〉에서 골라 쓰시오.

> ┤ 보기 ├
> flames / material / absorbs /
> pressure / experiment

(1) Apply _____ to the wound to stop the bleeding.
(2) They tried to put out the fire, but the _____ grew higher.
(3) The sponge _____ water.
(4) Steel is an essential _____ in building.
(5) Students are doing a science _____ with a candle.

**[04~05]** 다음 대화를 읽고 물음에 답하시오.

Minsu: What are you reading, Jiwon?
Jiwon: I'm reading a book about magic and science.
Minsu: That sounds interesting.
Jiwon: Yes. This book introduces 100 magic tricks that use science. I've learned about half of (A)them.
Minsu: That's cool. Can you show me some of the tricks?
Jiwon: Sure. I can show you a balloon trick now.
Minsu: Great! I can't wait to see it.

**04** 위 대화의 밑줄 친 (A)them이 가리키는 것을 찾아 쓰시오.

➡ _____

**05** 위 대화의 내용과 일치하지 <u>않는</u> 것은?

① 지원이는 마술과 과학에 관한 책을 읽고 있다.
② 책은 과학을 사용하는 100가지 마술을 소개하고 있다.
③ 지원이는 책에서 소개한 마술 중 절반 정도를 익혔다.
④ 지원이는 풍선 마술을 보여 줄 수 있다.
⑤ 민수는 지원이가 소개한 책을 빨리 읽고 싶다.

**[06~07]** 다음 대화를 읽고 물음에 답하시오.

Brian: Mina, will you join our tennis club?
Mina: It sounds interesting, but I signed up for a special class this fall.
Brian: Which class did you sign up for?
Mina: I signed up for a magic class.    (A)
Brian: That sounds cool! Have you learned magic tricks before?
Mina: Yes, I learned some before, but I need more practice.
Brian: I hope I can see your magic tricks some day.

**06** 〈보기〉에 주어진 단어들을 모두 배열하여 위 대화의 빈칸 (A)에 쓰시오.

> ┌── 보기 ──┐
> tricks / new / there / can't / to / I / wait / learn / magic

➡ _____

**07** 위 대화의 내용과 일치하지 <u>않는</u> 것은?

① 미나는 이번 가을에 특별 수업에 등록했다.
② 미나는 마술 수업에 등록했다.
③ 미나는 새로운 마술 묘기를 빨리 배우고 싶어 한다.
④ 미나는 전에 마술 묘기를 배운 적이 없다.
⑤ Brian은 언젠가 미나의 마술 묘기를 볼 수 있기를 바란다.

**08** 다음 대화의 밑줄 친 (A)와 바꾸어 쓸 수 있는 것은?

> **Jaemin:** Ms. Jeong, does a glass of water weigh more when there's a fish in it?
> **Ms. Jeong:** Yes, it does. We can test it now.
> **Jaemin:** But how? We don't have a fish.
> **Ms. Jeong:** We can use a finger instead of a fish.
> **Jaemin:** How will that work?
> **Ms. Jeong:** I'll weigh a glass of water first. Then I will put my finger in the water and weigh it to compare.
> **Jaemin:** Oh, (A)<u>I can't wait to see the difference.</u>

① I don't have time to wait to see the difference.
② I'm not able to see the difference.
③ I'm looking forward to seeing the difference.
④ I'm doubtful if there is the difference.
⑤ I don't know how to tell the difference.

**[09~10]** 다음 글을 읽고 물음에 답하시오.

> **Jane:** Today we'll make ice cream. ⓐ<u>Which</u> flavor do you want to make? How about strawberry? First, ⓑ<u>mix</u> two cups of milk, two cups of heavy cream, and half a cup of sugar. Next, cut five strawberries into small pieces. Then, mix everything together and ⓒ<u>putting</u> it in the freezer. That's it. It's easy ⓓ<u>to make</u>, isn't it? Why don't you try ⓔ<u>making</u> it at home?

**09** 위 대화의 밑줄 친 ⓐ~ⓔ 중 어법상 어색한 것을 찾아 바르게 고치시오.

➡ _____

**10** 위 글을 읽고 대답할 수 <u>없는</u> 것은?

① Which flavor ice cream is Jane going to make?
② What should Jane prepare to make the ice cream?
③ How much milk does Jane need to make the ice cream?
④ What should Jane do after cutting five strawberries into small pieces?
⑤ How long should Jane keep the mix in the freezer?

**[11~12]** 다음 대화를 읽고 물음에 답하시오.

> **Brian:** Yujin, why did you put the eggs in water?
> **Yujin:** I'm picking out the bad eggs.
> **Brian:** Which eggs are fresh, and which ones are not?
> **Yujin:** Eggs that sink in water are fresh. When eggs float in water, they're not fresh. You shouldn't eat them.
> **Brian:** That's interesting. Why do the bad eggs float?
> **Yujin:** Because they have gas inside. The gas acts like the air in a balloon.
> **Brian:** Oh, I see.

**11** Which eggs are not fresh?

➡ _____

**12** What makes the bad eggs float in the water?

➡ _____

**13** 다음 빈칸에 들어갈 말이 바르게 짝지어진 것은?

(A) _____ it is so cold here?
(B) It is clever _____ her to know the answer.

① Why – to        ② Why – for
③ How come – in   ④ How come – of
⑤ How come – to

**14** 다음 중 어법상 바르지 <u>않은</u> 것은?

① It is nice of her to give you a candy.
② How come you are so busy these days?
③ It is considerate of her to do the volunteer work.
④ Why did you throw away the paper?
⑤ It is possible of him to ride a bike alone.

**15** 다음 중 밑줄 친 부분의 쓰임이 <u>다른</u> 하나는?

① <u>It</u> is dangerous for you to be alone in the playground.
② <u>It</u> is foolish of her to believe such a thing.
③ <u>It</u> is my duty to protect you.
④ <u>It</u> is a great idea to invent something to make your life comfortable.
⑤ <u>It</u> was very dark in the forest and the girl couldn't find the way.

**16** 다음 빈칸에 알맞은 말을 쓰시오.

그가 너의 생일에 축하하지 않은 것은 인색했어.
➡ It was mean _____ _____ _____ _____ say congratulations on your birthday.

**17** 주어진 단어를 활용하여 다음 우리말을 영어로 쓰시오.

도대체 왜 그는 파티에 오지 않는 거야?
(how / to the party)

➡ _____

**[18~19]** 다음 글을 읽고 물음에 답하시오.

Jina: Wow! How come the water disappeared?
Ken: (A) Then the jelly stuck to the bottom.
(B) Before the trick, I put a special material into one of the cups.
(C) Therefore, if you want to try this trick, it's necessary to use cups that you can't see through.
(D) The material absorbed the water and turned it into jelly.
Jina: Thank you for your great performance. It was really amazing!

**18** 자연스러운 글이 되도록 (A)~(D)를 바르게 배열하시오.

➡ _____

**19** 다음은 위 마술의 원리를 요약한 것이다. 빈칸에 알맞은 말을 쓰시오.

> The special material in the cup _____ the water and turned it into jelly. Then the jelly _____ to _____ _____.

**[20~21]** 다음 글을 읽고 물음에 답하시오.

Jina: Welcome to the Super Science Magic Show! It's always exciting to see magic tricks. And it's more exciting to find out the secrets behind them. Some people think the secret of magic is science. Today, Ken, a member of the School Magic Club, will use science to perform his tricks. Which tricks will he show us? (A)I can't wait to see them.

**20** According to Jina, what will Ken use to perform his tricks? Answer in English with a full sentence.

➡ _____

**21** 다음 중 밑줄 친 (A)가 의미하는 것으로 가장 적절한 것은?

① I have been waiting for Ken for a long time.
② I don't have any interest in seeing a magic show.
③ I am really looking forward to seeing them.
④ I want Ken to show us many tricks more often.
⑤ I can't help seeing the show as soon as possible.

**[22~25]** 다음 글을 읽고 물음에 답하시오.

Ken: Hello, everyone. Today, I'm going to ① show you something amazing. ②Here's a dish with water in it. Now, I'll put a candle in the middle of the dish. Next, I'll light the candle and cover ③it with a glass. "Abracadabra!"
Jina: Look at the water! ④Why it rose into the glass?
Ken: Air expands when it gets hot and creates ⑤higher pressure. When it gets cold, air contracts and creates lower pressure. When the flame burnt out, the air inside the glass cooled down. As the air cooled down, the air pressure dropped. So the air outside the glass was at a higher pressure. It pushed the water into the glass.

**22** 위 글의 ①~⑤ 중 어법상 바르지 않은 것은?

①        ②        ③        ④        ⑤

**23** What happened to the water after the flame in the glass burnt out?

➡ _____

**24** 위 글을 읽고 답할 수 없는 것은?

① What happens when air gets cold?
② What should we do if we want air to contract?
③ When does air expand?
④ Why did the air pressure inside the glass drop?
⑤ How long did the candle burn?

**25** What did Ken do after lighting the candle? Answer in English with a full sentence.

➡ _____

## Lesson 8

# Call It Courage

 **의사소통 기능**

- 알고 있는지 묻기

  Have you heard of the Gobi Desert?
  Have you heard about the soccer match on Saturday?

- 격려하기

  Don't give up!

**언어 형식**

- 사역동사

  My mom **made** me **clean** my room.

- Although

  **Although** it was raining, I played soccer.

# Words & Expressions

## Key Words

- **achievement**[ətʃíːvmənt] 명 성과
- **against**[əgénst] 전 ~에 맞서
- **although**[ɔːlðóu] 접 비록 ~일지라도
- **amazing**[əméiziŋ] 형 놀라운
- **bare**[bɛər] 형 벌거벗은, 맨 ~
- **bat**[bæt] 명 배트
- **care**[kɛər] 동 걱정하다, 관심을 갖다
- **completely**[kəmplíːtli] 부 완전히
- **courage**[kə́ːridʒ] 명 용기
- **cross**[krɔːs] 동 건너다, 가로지르다, 횡단하다
- **decide**[disáid] 동 결정하다, 결심하다
- **desert**[dézərt] 명 사막
- **discouraged**[diskə́ːridʒd] 형 낙담한
- **everywhere**[évriwer] 부 모든 곳에, 어디나
- **excellent**[éksələnt] 형 훌륭한
- **exercise**[éksərsàiz] 동 운동하다
- **experience**[ikspíəriəns] 동 경험하다
- **floating**[flóutiŋ] 형 떠 있는
- **gather**[gǽðər] 동 모으다, 모이다
- **healthy**[hélθi] 형 건강한
- **ice hockey** 아이스하키

- **impossible**[impásəbl] 형 불가능한
- **lose**[luːz] 동 지다, 잃다
- **match**[mætʃ] 명 경기
- **meal**[miːl] 명 식사, 끼니
- **nail**[neil] 동 못질하다 명 못
- **proud**[praud] 형 자랑스러워하는
- **semi-final**[sèmifáinl] 명 준결승전
- **shaky**[ʃéiki] 형 흔들리는, 휘청거리는
- **shoot**[ʃuːt] 동 슛하다
- **shout**[ʃaut] 동 소리 지르다, 소리치다
- **slippery**[slípəri] 형 미끄러운
- **still**[stil] 부 그럼에도, 하지만, 여전히
- **sweater**[swétər] 명 스웨터
- **tournament**[túərnəmənt] 명 토너먼트
- **ugly**[ʌ́gli] 형 못생긴, 추한
- **village**[vílidʒ] 명 마을
- **villager**[vílidʒər] 명 마을 사람
- **wash**[wɑʃ] 동 씻다
- **weak**[wiːk] 형 약한
- **wide**[waid] 형 넓은
- **windy**[wíndi] 형 바람이 센

## Key Expressions

- **be about to** 막 ~하려고 하다
- **be good at** ~을 잘하다
- **fall into** ~에 빠지다
- **give it a try** 시도해 보다
- **give up** 포기하다
- **in fact** 사실은

- **in front of** ~의 앞에
- **laugh at** ~을 비웃다
- **on foot** 걸어서, 도보로
- **take off** ~을 벗다
- **try[do] one's best** 최선을 다하다
- **try out for** ~을 지원하다

## Word Power

※ 서로 반대되는 뜻을 가진 어휘

☐ **encouraged** 용기를 북돋운 ↔ **discouraged** 낙담한

☐ **healthy** 건강한 ↔ **unhealthy** 건강하지 않은

☐ **weak** 약한 ↔ **strong** 강한

☐ **ugly** 못생긴 ↔ **handsome** 잘생긴

☐ **wide** 넓은 ↔ **narrow** 좁은

☐ **possible** 가능한 ↔ **impossible** 불가능한

☐ **win** 이기다 ↔ **lose** 지다

☐ **gather** 모이다, 모으다 ↔ **spread** 퍼지다

☐ **inside** 안에 ↔ **outside** 밖에

☐ **in front of** ~의 앞에 ↔ **behind** ~ 뒤에

## English Dictionary

☐ **achievement** 성과
→ a thing done successfully, typically by effort, courage, or skill
일반적으로 노력, 용기 또는 기술에 의해 성공적으로 이루어진 것

☐ **bare** 벌거벗은
→ not covered by clothes
옷에 의해 덮여지지 않은

☐ **courage** 용기
→ the quality of being brave when you are facing a difficult or dangerous situation, or when you are very ill
당신이 어려움 또는 위험한 상황을 마주하고 있을 때 또는 당신이 매우 아플 때 용감해 지는 자질

☐ **discouraged** 낙담한
→ no longer having the confidence you need to continue doing something
무언가를 계속하기 위해 당신이 필요한 자신감을 더 이상 갖고 있지 않은

☐ **gather** 모으다
→ to get things from different places and put them together in one place
다른 장소들에서 물건을 구해서 그것들을 한 장소에 함께 놓다

☐ **impossible** 불가능한
→ unable to be done or to happen
이루어지거나 일어날 수 없는

☐ **lose** 지다
→ to fail to win a game
경기에서 이기지 못하다

☐ **match** 경기
→ a contest between two or more players or teams
둘 또는 그 이상의 선수들이나 팀들 간의 경쟁

☐ **nail** 못질하다
→ to fasten something to something else with nails
못으로 어떤 것을 다른 어떤 것에 고정시키다

☐ **proud** 자랑스러워하는
→ feeling pleased about something that you have done or something that you own
당신이 한 것 또는 당신이 소유한 것에 대해 즐거움을 느끼는

☐ **shaky** 흔들리는, 휘청거리는
→ not firm or steady
확고하거나 꾸준하지 않은

☐ **shoot** 슛하다
→ to kick or throw a ball in a sport such as football or basketball towards the place where you can get a point
축구 또는 농구 같은 운동에서 당신이 득점할 수 있는 곳을 향해 공을 차거나 던지다

☐ **villager** 마을 사람
→ someone who lives in a village
마을에 사는 사람

☐ **weak** 약한
→ not physically strong
신체적으로 강하지 않은

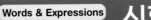 

**서답형**

**01** 다음 짝지어진 단어의 관계가 같도록 빈칸에 알맞은 말을 쓰시오.

> wide : narrow = strong : _____

**02** 다음 영영풀이가 가리키는 것을 고르시오.

> not covered by clothes

① bear    ② bare    ③ still

④ proud    ⑤ care

**중요**

**03** 다음 중 밑줄 친 부분의 뜻풀이가 바르지 <u>않은</u> 것은?

① I was <u>completely</u> surprised by the news. 완전히

② My brother <u>gathered</u> more wood while I prepared a fire. 모았다

③ Can you <u>nail</u> this sign to a tree? 손톱

④ The board was <u>shaky</u> when I went up to dive. 흔들리는

⑤ I looked <u>everywhere</u> for my key but I couldn't find it. 모든 곳에

**서답형**

**04** 다음 문장의 빈칸에 들어갈 말을 〈보기〉에서 골라 쓰시오.

> ┌── 보기 ──┐
> exercise / deserts / experience / cross / healthy

(1) Not much water can be found in _____.

(2) You should _____ the street at a green light.

(3) I don't want to _____ riding that roller coaster.

(4) I want to live a _____ life.

(5) I try to _____ at least three times a week.

**서답형**

**05** 다음 우리말에 맞게 빈칸에 알맞은 말을 쓰시오.

(1) Jane은 시험에서 최선을 다했다.

➡ Jane _____ _____ _____ at the test.

(2) 사실 그들은 훌륭한 기술을 쌓았다.

➡ _____ _____, they built excellent skills.

(3) 사람들은 그들의 생각을 비웃었다.

➡ People _____ _____ their idea.

(4) 그들은 시도해 보기로 결심했다.

➡ They decided to _____ _____ _____ _____.

(5) 그들이 막 떠나려고 했을 때, 마을 사람들이 그들에게 새 신발을 주었다.

➡ When they _____ _____ _____ leave, the villagers gave them new shoes.

**중요**

**06** 다음 주어진 문장의 밑줄 친 cross와 다른 의미로 쓰인 것은?

> I don't want to <u>cross</u> the desert on foot.

① We <u>crossed</u> the road and joined Jack.

② Waving her hand, she <u>crossed</u> the bridge.

③ Don't <u>cross</u> the street here.

④ Jack finally <u>crossed</u> the finishing line.

⑤ I'm always wearing my <u>cross</u> necklace.

**01** 다음 짝지어진 단어의 관계가 같도록 빈칸에 알맞은 말을 쓰시오.

> inside : outside = encouraged : _____

**02** 다음 우리말에 맞게 빈칸에 알맞은 말을 쓰시오.

(1) 후반전에 그들은 신발을 벗었다.
  ➡ They _____ _____ their shoes during the second half.

(2) 나는 도서관 앞에서 Tom을 기다렸다.
  ➡ I waited for Tom _____ _____ _____ the library.

(3) 그는 걸어서 학교에 간다.
  ➡ He goes to school _____ _____.

(4) 공과 소년들은 종종 바다에 빠지곤 했다.
  ➡ The ball and the boys would often _____ _____ the sea.

**03** 다음 문장의 빈칸에 들어갈 말을 〈보기〉에서 골라 쓰시오.

> ┤ 보기 ├
> weak / meals / lose / match / against

(1) Did you see the soccer _____ last night?

(2) We'll play _____ the other team in the afternoon.

(3) My legs felt _____ after running for an hour.

(4) We might _____ if we don't play as a team.

(5) My pet eats five _____ a day.

**04** 다음 우리말과 일치하도록 주어진 어구를 모두 배열하여 영작하시오.

(1) 길을 따라 걷는 동안 나는 구멍에 빠졌다.
  (hole / I / the / a / along / into / road / while / fell / walking)
  ➡ _____

(2) 열심히 노력하고 절대 포기해서는 안 된다.
  (never / and / hard / you / up / should / try / give)
  ➡ _____

(3) 외투를 벗지 마세요.
  (off / don't / coat / your / take)
  ➡ _____

**05** 다음 문장의 빈칸에 들어갈 말을 〈보기〉에서 골라 쓰시오.

> ┤ 보기 ├
> laughed at / tried out for / give up / is good at / in fact

(1) Sarah _____ _____ _____ the cheerleading squad.

(2) You shouldn't _____ _____ no matter how difficult it is.

(3) People _____ _____ my painting but I was proud of myself for completing it.

(4) We thought the questions were hard. _____ _____, they were easy.

(5) Brian _____ _____ _____ drawing pictures.

교과서
# Conversation

**1** 알고 있는지 묻기

- Have you heard of the Gobi Desert? 고비 사막에 대해 들어 봤니?
- Have you heard about the soccer match on Saturday? 토요일 축구 경기에 대해 들어 봤니?

■ 'Have you heard of / about …?'은 '너는 …에 대해 들어 봤니?'라는 뜻으로, 상대방이 어떤 것을 알고 있는지 묻는 표현이다. 'Have you heard' 다음에 of가 오는 경우는 어떤 사실, 사물, 사람의 존재 자체를 아는지 물을 때 사용한다. about의 경우는 어떤 행사나 사람이 한 일을 구체적으로 아는지 물을 때 사용한다. 이에 대한 대답으로 긍정일 때는 'Yes, I have.', 부정일 때는 'No, I haven't.'로 대답한다.

### 알고 있는지 묻기

- Have you heard about Thomas Edison? Thomas Edison에 대해 들어 봤니?
- Do you know how to keep your health? 건강을 지키는 법을 아니?

### 알고 있는지 대답하기

- I've been told about my new English teacher. 나는 나의 새 영어 선생님에 대해 들었다.
- I'm aware of what's going on. 나는 무슨 일이 일어나고 있는지 알고 있다.

### 핵심 Check

1. 다음 우리말과 일치하도록 빈칸에 알맞은 말을 쓰시오.

(1) A: _____ _____ _____ of cricket? (cricket에 대해 들어 본 적이 있나요?)

   B: No, I haven't. (아니요. 들어 본 적 없어요.)

(2) A: Have you heard of Beethoven? (베토벤에 대해 들어 본 적이 있나요?)

   B: _____, _____ _____. (예. 들어 보았어요.)

(3) A: Have you heard of Anthony Webb? (Anthony Webb에 대해 들어 본 적이 있나요?)

   B: _____, _____ _____. Who is he? (아니요, 들어 본 적 없어요. 그가 누구인데요?)

**2** 격려하기

Don't give up! 포기하지 마!

■ 어떤 사람을 격려할 때 'Don't give up!'이라는 표현을 쓰는데 이것 이외에도, 'You can do it!', 'You'll do better next time.' 등의 표현을 사용할 수 있다.

### 격려하기

- There's always a next time. 항상 다음 기회가 있어.
- Cheer up! 기운 내!
- You can do it! 너는 할 수 있어!
- Don't give up! 포기하지 마!
- Don't be so hard on yourself. 너무 자책하지 마.
- Don't take it too hard. 너무 상심하지 마.
- You are a great player. 너는 훌륭한 선수야.

### 핵심 Check

2. 다음 우리말과 일치하도록 빈칸에 알맞은 말을 쓰시오.

(1) A: I'd like to play soccer well, but it's not easy. (나는 축구를 잘하고 싶어, 근데 쉽지 않아.)

　　B: _____ _____ _____ _____ _____. You are a great player.

　　(너무 상심하지 마. 너는 훌륭한 선수야.)

(2) A: I didn't do well in the match. My shoot was so weak.

　　(나는 시합에서 잘하지 못했어. 내 슛은 너무 약했어.)

　　B: _____ _____ _____ _____ _____ _____. (너무 자책하지 마.)

(3) A: We are a weak team, so everyone thinks that we are going to lose.

　　(우리는 약한 팀이야. 그래서 모든 사람들이 우리가 질 거라고 생각해.)

　　B: _____ _____! _____ _____ _____ _____! (기운 내! 너는 할 수 있어!)

### Listen & Speak 1 A

G: Tim, ❶have you heard of the Gobi Desert?

B: Yes, I have. Isn't it in Mongolia and China?

G: Yes, it is. Yesterday, I saw a TV show about people ❷who crossed the desert ❸on foot.

B: Only on foot?

G: Yes, it took them about 51 days.

B: Wow, that's amazing. I want to experience life in the desert but I don't want to cross ❹it on foot.

G: Well, I want to try and cross the Gobi Desert in 50 days.

G: Tim, 너는 고비 사막에 대해 들어 봤니?

B: 응, 들어 봤어. 그것은 몽골과 중국에 있지 않니?

G: 응, 맞아. 어제 나는 걸어서 그 사막을 건넌 사람들에 관한 TV 쇼를 봤어.

B: 단지 걸어서만?

G: 응, 51일 정도 걸렸어.

B: 와, 놀랍다. 나는 사막에서의 삶을 경험하고 싶지만 그곳을 걸어서 건너고 싶지는 않아.

G: 음, 나는 시도해 보고 싶고 고비 사막을 50일 내로 건너고 싶어.

❶ 'Have you heard of / about ...?'은 '너는 ...을 들어 봤니?'라는 뜻으로, 상대방이 어떤 것을 알고 있는지 묻는 표현이다.
❷ who는 선행사 people에 대한 주격 관계대명사이다.
❸ on foot: 걸어서, 도보로
❹ it은 the desert, 즉 고비 사막을 가리킨다.

**Check(√) True or False**

(1) The Gobi Desert is in Mongolia and China.      T ☐ F ☐

(2) The girl crossed the desert on foot in 51 days.      T ☐ F ☐

### Listen & Speak 2 A

W: What can you do to be healthy? First, ❶try to exercise every day. Second, try to eat healthy food. Don't eat too much fast food. Third, wash your hands before ❷meals. Do ❸these tips sound hard to do? Well, take one step ❹at a time and don't ❺give up. Then you'll live a healthy life.

W: 당신은 건강해지기 위해 무엇을 할 수 있는가? 먼저, 매일 운동하도록 해라. 둘째, 건강에 좋은 음식을 먹도록 해라. 패스트푸드를 너무 많이 먹지 마라. 셋째, 식사 전에 손을 씻어라. 이 조언들이 실천하기에 어렵게 들리는가? 음, 한 번에 하나씩 행하고 포기하지 마라. 그러면 당신은 건강한 삶을 살 것이다.

❶ try to ~: ~하려고 노력하다, 애쓰다
❷ meal: 식사
❸ these tips는 앞에서 언급한 3가지 조언들을 가리킨다.
❹ at a time: 한번에
❺ give up: 포기하다

**Check(√) True or False**

(3) The woman explains how to be healthy.      T ☐ F ☐

(4) It is not good for your health to eat too much fast food.      T ☐ F ☐

**Listen & Speak 1 B**

G: Alex, have you heard about this year's "Ugly Sweater Party?"

B: ❶Of course, I have. It's on December 5th, right?

G: That's right. Are you going to go?

B: I want to, but I don't have an ugly sweater.

G: I have ❷one ❸that I don't wear at home. You can have it if you want.

B: Thanks. That would be great.

G: Let's meet ❹in front of the Student Center and go inside together.

B: Sure. See you then.

❶ 알고 있음을 대답하는 것으로 'Yes, I have.'로 바꾸어 쓸 수 있다.
❷ one은 an ugly sweater를 가리킨다.
❸ 목적격 관계대명사로 which로 바꾸어 쓸 수 있다.
❹ in front of: ~ 앞에

 **Real Life Communication A**

Father: Emily, are you excited about your match on Saturday?

Emily: Not really. We're playing ❶against a strong team. I think we'll lose.

Father: Don't say that. Have you heard about the Greek team in the 2004 Euro Cup?

Emily: ❷No, I haven't. What about them?

Father: They were a weak team, so everyone thought that they would ❸lose.

Emily: What happened?

Father: They played as a team and ❹worked hard. Finally, they won the Euro Cup. So, don't give up.

Emily: Thanks, Dad. We'll ❺try our best.

❶ against: ~에 맞서
❷ 들어 본 적이 없음을 가리킨다.
❸ lose 지다 ↔ win 이기다
❹ played와 병렬 구조이다.
❺ try[do] one's best: 최선을 다하다

 **Listen & Speak 2 B**

G: Hojun, are you going to ❶try out for the school ice hockey team? The new season ❷ is about to start.

B: ❸I'm not sure.

G: Why not?

B: I heard that Tony and Brad are also trying out for the team. They're so good.

G: Well, you're also good at ice hockey, so ❹ don't give up!

B: Okay, I'll try my best. ❺Thanks a lot.

❶ try out for: ~에 지원하다
❷ be about to ~: 막 ~하려고 하다
❸ I'm not sure.: 잘 모르겠어. (확신이 없음을 나타내는 표현)
❹ 격려하는 표현으로 'Cheer up!' 등으로 바꾸어 쓸 수 있다.
❺ Thanks a lot. = Thank you very much.

 **Let's Check ❶**

B: Have you heard of Thomas Edison? When he was young, he couldn't read well. Also, he lost all of the ❶hearing in his left ear. ❷Still, he became a great scientist. Although you may have difficulties, be ❸like Edison and don't give up.

❶ hearing: 청각, 청력
❷ still은 '그럼에도'를 의미하며 'Nevertheless'로 바꾸어 쓸 수 있다.
❸ like: ~처럼

● 다음 우리말과 일치하도록 빈칸에 알맞은 말을 쓰시오.

### Listen & Speak 1 A

G: Tim, _____ _____ _____ of the Gobi Desert?

B: Yes, I _____. Isn't it in Mongolia and China?

G: Yes, it is. Yesterday, I saw a TV show about people _____ _____ the desert _____ _____.

B: Only on foot?

G: Yes, it _____ them _____ 51 days.

B: Wow, that's amazing. I want to _____ life in the _____ but I don't want to _____ it on foot.

G: Well, I want to _____ and cross the Gobi Desert _____ 50 days.

**해석**

G: Tim, 너는 고비 사막에 대해 들어 봤니?

B: 응, 들어 봤어. 그것은 몽골과 중국에 있지 않니?

G: 응, 맞아. 어제 나는 걸어서 그 사막을 건넌 사람들에 관한 TV 쇼를 봤어.

B: 단지 걸어서만?

G: 응, 51일 정도 걸렸어.

B: 와, 놀랍다. 나는 사막에서의 삶을 경험하고 싶지만 그곳을 걸어서 건너고 싶지는 않아.

G: 음, 나는 시도해 보고 싶고 고비 사막을 50일 내로 건너고 싶어.

### Listen & Speak 1 B

G: Alex, _____ _____ _____ _____ this year's "Ugly Sweater Party?"

B: Of course, I _____. It's _____ December 5th, right?

G: That's _____. Are you going to go?

B: I _____ _____, but I don't have an ugly sweater.

G: I have one that _____ _____ _____ _____ _____. You can have it _____ _____ _____.

B: Thanks. That would be great.

G: Let's meet _____ _____ _____ the Student Center and _____ _____ together.

B: Sure. _____ you then.

G: Alex, 너는 올해의 "못생긴 스웨터 파티"에 대해 들어 봤니?

B: 물론 들어 봤어. 그것은 12월 5일에 열려, 맞지?

G: 맞아. 너 갈 거니?

B: 가고 싶지만 나는 못생긴 스웨터가 없어.

G: 집에 내가 입지 않는 스웨터가 한 벌 있어. 네가 원하면 그걸 가져도 좋아.

B: 고마워. 그래주면 좋겠어.

G: 학생회관 앞에서 만나서 같이 들어가자.

B: 그래. 그때 보자.

### Listen & Speak 2 A

W: What can you do to be _____? First, try to _____ every day. Second, _____ _____ eat healthy food. _____ _____ too much fast food. Third, _____ your hands before _____. Do these tips _____ _____ to do? Well, _____ one _____ at a time and don't _____ _____. Then you'll _____ a healthy _____.

W: 당신은 건강해지기 위해 무엇을 할 수 있는가? 먼저, 매일 운동하도록 해라. 둘째, 건강에 좋은 음식을 먹도록 해라. 패스트푸드를 너무 많이 먹지 마라. 셋째, 식사 전에 손을 씻어라. 이 조언들이 실천하기에 어렵게 들리는가? 음, 한 번에 하나씩 행하고 포기하지 마라. 그러면 당신은 건강한 삶을 살 것이다.

## Listen & Speak 2 B

G: Hojun, are you going to _____ _____ _____ the school ice hockey team? The new season is _____ to start.

B: I'm not _____.

G: _____ _____?

B: I heard that Tony and Brad are also _____ _____ _____ the team. They're so good.

G: Well, you're also _____ _____ ice hockey, so _____ _____ _____!

B: Okay, I'll _____ _____ _____. Thanks a lot.

G: 호준아, 너 학교 아이스하키 팀에 지원할 예정이니? 새 시즌이 곧 시작돼.

B: 잘 모르겠어.

G: 왜 몰라?

B: Tony와 Brad도 그 팀에 지원할 거라고 들었어. 그들은 굉장히 잘해.

G: 음, 너 또한 아이스하키를 잘하잖아, 그러니 포기하지 마!

B: 알았어, 최선을 다할게. 정말 고마워.

## Real Life Communication

Father: Emily, are you _____ about your _____ on Saturday?

Emily: Not really. We're playing _____ a strong team. I think we'll _____.

Father: Don't say that. _____ _____ _____ about the Greek team in the 2004 Euro Cup?

Emily: _____, I _____. What _____ them?

Father: They were a weak team, _____ everyone thought that they would _____.

Emily: _____ _____?

Father: They played as a team and _____ _____. Finally, they _____ the Euro Cup. So, don't _____ _____.

Emily: Thanks, Dad. We'll _____ _____ _____.

Father: Emily, 토요일에 있을 경기에 대해 설레니?

Emily: 그렇진 않아요. 우리는 강한 팀에 맞서 시합할 거예요. 우리가 질 것 같아요.

Father: 그렇게 말하지 마. 너는 2004 유로컵에서 그리스 팀에 대해 들어 봤니?

Emily: 아니요, 들어본 적 없어요. 그들이 어땠는데요?

Father: 그들은 약한 팀이었어, 그래서 모두가 그들이 질 거라고 생각했지.

Emily: 무슨 일이 일어났는데요?

Father: 그들은 한 팀으로 경기하며 열심히 노력했어. 결국 그들은 유로컵에서 우승했단다. 그러니 포기하지 마.

Emily: 감사해요, 아빠. 우리도 최선을 다할게요.

## Let's Check ❶

B: _____ _____ _____ _____ Thomas Edison? When he was young, he couldn't _____ _____. Also, he _____ all of the _____ _____ his left ear. _____, he became a great scientist. Although you may have _____, _____ _____ _____ Edison and _____ _____ _____.

B: 당신은 Thomas Edison에 대해 들어 봤나요? 어렸을 때 그는 글을 잘 읽지 못했습니다. 또한 그는 왼쪽 귀가 전혀 들리지 않았습니다. 그럼에도 그는 위대한 과학자가 되었습니다. 당신이 어려움을 갖고 있을지라도, Edison처럼 되고 포기하지 마세요.

**[01~02]** 다음 글을 읽고 물음에 답하시오.

> B: (A)당신은 Thomas Edison에 대해 들어 봤나요?(of, have) When he was young, he couldn't read well. Also, he lost all of the hearing in his left ear. (B)Still, he became a great scientist. Although you may have difficulties, be like Edison and don't give up.

**01** 위 글의 밑줄 친 (A)의 우리말을 주어진 단어를 사용하여 영작하시오.

➡ _____

**02** 위 글의 밑줄 친 (B)Still과 같은 뜻으로 쓰인 것은?

① Even though I had some bread, I'm still hungry.

② The weather was cold and wet. Still, we had a great time together.

③ Do you still live in the same city?

④ I'm still waiting for his reply.

⑤ Are you still using this old pen?

**[03~04]** 다음 글을 읽고 물음에 답하시오.

> W: What can you do to be healthy? First, try to exercise every day. (A) Second, try to eat healthy food. (B) Don't eat too much fast food. (C) Third, wash your hands before meals. (D) Well, take one step at a time and don't give up. (E) Then you'll live a healthy life.

**03** 위 글의 (A)~(E) 중 주어진 문장이 들어가기에 적절한 곳은?

> Do these tips sound hard to do?

① (A)     ② (B)     ③ (C)     ④ (D)     ⑤ (E)

**04** 위 글의 내용과 일치하지 <u>않는</u> 것은?

① 여자는 건강해지는 법에 대해 설명하고 있다.

② 여자는 매일 운동을 할 것을 조언하였다.

③ 여자는 건강에 좋은 음식을 먹도록 조언하였다.

④ 여자는 식사 전에 손을 씻을 것을 조언하였다.

⑤ 여자의 조언들은 실천하기가 어렵지 않다.

[01~03] 다음 대화를 읽고 물음에 답하시오.

> Mina: Tim, have you heard of the Gobi Desert?
> Tim: Yes, I (A)[did / have]. Isn't it in Mongolia and China?
> Mina: Yes, it is. Yesterday, I saw a TV show about people (B)[which / who] crossed the desert on foot.
> Tim: Only on foot?
> Mina: Yes, it took them about 51 days.
> Tim: Wow, that's amazing. I want to experience life in the desert (C)[but / and] I don't want to cross it on foot.
> Mina: Well, I want to try and cross the Gobi Desert in 50 days.

**서답형**

**01** 위 대화에서 다음의 영영풀이가 가리키는 것을 찾아 쓰시오.

> an area of very dry land that is usually covered with sand and is very hot

➡ _____

**02** 위 대화의 괄호 (A)~(C)에 들어갈 말이 바르게 짝지어진 것은?

① did – which – but
② did – who – and
③ have – who – but
④ have – who – and
⑤ have – which – but

**중요**

**03** 위 글의 내용과 일치하지 <u>않는</u> 것은?

① Tim은 고비 사막에 대해 들어 봤다.
② 고비 사막은 몽골과 중국에 있다.
③ 미나는 어제 걸어서 사막을 건넌 사람들에 관한 TV 쇼를 봤다.
④ 사람들이 걸어서 고비 사막을 건너는 데 약 51일 정도 걸렸다.
⑤ Tim은 사막에서의 삶을 경험하고 걸어서 고비 사막을 건너고 싶어 한다.

**서답형**

**04** 다음 대화에서 (A)~(E)가 자연스럽게 이어지도록 순서대로 배열하시오.

> Father: Emily, are you excited about your match on Saturday?
> Emily: Not really. We're playing against a strong team. I think we'll lose.

> (A) What happened?
> (B) No, I haven't. What about them?
> (C) They played as a team and worked hard. Finally, they won the Euro Cup. So, don't give up.
> (D) They were a weak team, so everyone thought that they would lose.
> (E) Don't say that. Have you heard about the Greek team in the 2004 Euro Cup?

> Emily: Thanks, Dad. We'll try our best.

➡ _____

[05~06] 다음 글을 읽고 물음에 답하시오.

> W: What can you do to be ⓐ<u>healthy</u>? First, try to exercise every day. Second, try to eat healthy food. Don't eat too much ⓑ <u>fast food</u>. Third, wash your hands ⓒ <u>before</u> meals. Do these tips sound ⓓ<u>hard</u> to do? Well, take one step at a time and ⓔ <u>give up</u>. Then you'll live a healthy life.

**서답형**

**05** 위 글의 밑줄 친 ⓐ~ⓔ 중 내용의 흐름상 어색한 것을 찾아 바르게 고치시오.

➡ _____

**서답형**

**06** 위 글에서 제시한 건강한 삶을 살기 위한 조언 3가지를 찾아 우리말로 간단하게 설명하시오.

➡ _____

_____

[07~08] 다음 대화를 읽고 물음에 답하시오.

> Suji: Hojun, are you going to try out for the school ice hockey team? The new season is about to start.
>
> Hojun: I'm not sure.
>
> Suji: Why not?
>
> Hojun: I heard that Tony and Brad are also trying out for the team. They're so good.
>
> Suji: Well, you're also good at ice hockey, so _____!
>
> Hojun: Okay, I'll try my best. Thanks a lot.

**07** 위 대화의 빈칸에 들어갈 말로 적절한 것은?

① don't give up
② don't try out for it
③ that's a relief
④ please forgive me
⑤ forget it

**08** 위 대화의 내용과 일치하지 <u>않는</u> 것은?

① Tony와 Brad가 학교 아이스하키 팀에 지원한다.
② 아이스하키 팀의 새로운 시즌이 곧 시작된다.
③ 호준이는 학교 아이스하키 팀에 지원할지 고민 중이다.
④ Tony와 Brad는 아이스하키를 아주 잘한다.
⑤ 호준이는 아이스하키 경기에 최선을 다할 것이다.

[09~10] 다음 대화를 읽고 물음에 답하시오.

> Sora: Alex, have you heard about this year's "Ugly Sweater Party?"
>
> Alex: Of course, I have. It's on December 5th, right?
>
> Sora: That's right. Are you going to go?
>
> Alex: I want to, but I don't have an ugly sweater.
>
> Sora: I have one that I don't wear at home. You can have it if you want.
>
> Alex: Thanks. That would be great.
>
> Sora: Let's meet in front of the Student Center and go inside together.
>
> Alex: Sure. See you then.

**09** 위 대화에서 나타난 Alex의 심경 변화로 적절한 것은?

① depressed → worried
② depressed → pleased
③ pleased → worried
④ pleased → satisfied
⑤ satisfied → dissatisfied

**서답형**

**10** 위 대화의 내용과 일치하도록 빈칸을 완성하시오.

> Although Alex didn't have his own (A)_____ _____, he could go to "Ugly Sweater Party" because of (B)_____ help. He borrowed her sweater that (C)_____ _____ _____. He really appreciated her.

[01~02] 다음 대화를 읽고 물음에 답하시오.

Sora: Alex, have you ⓐheard about this year's "Ugly Sweater Party?"

Alex: Of course, I ⓑhave. It's ⓒon December 5th, right?

Sora: That's right. Are you going to go?

Alex: I want to, but I don't have an ugly sweater.

Sora: I have one ⓓwho I don't wear at home. You can have it if you want.

Alex: Thanks. That would be great.

Sora: Let's meet ⓔin front of the Student Center and go inside together.

Alex: Sure. See you then.

**01** 위 대화의 밑줄 친 ⓐ~ⓔ 중 어법상 어색한 것을 찾아 바르게 고치시오.

➡ _____

**02** 위 대화의 내용과 일치하도록 빈칸을 완성하시오.

<Ugly Sweater Party>
Date: _____
Time: 4pm – 6pm
Place: _____
Notice: You should wear _____
_____.

**03** 다음 〈보기〉에 주어진 단어들을 골라 빈칸의 알맞은 곳에 써서 대화를 완성하시오.

— 보기 —
tips / fast / take / exercise / meals /
healthy / wash

W: What can you do to be (1)_____? First, try to (2)_____ every day. Second, try to eat healthy food. Don't eat too much (3)_____ food. (4)_____ your hands before (5)_____. Do these (6)_____ sound hard to do? Well, (7)_____ one step at a time and don't give up. Then you'll live a healthy life.

[04~06] 다음 글을 읽고 물음에 답하시오.

B: ⓐHave you heard of Thomas Edison? When he was young, he couldn't read well. Also, he lost all of the ⓑhearing in his left ear. ⓒStill, he became a great scientist. ⓓDespite you may have difficulties, be ⓔlike Edison and 포기하지 마.

**04** 위 글의 밑줄 친 우리말을 세 단어로 영작하시오.

➡ _____

**05** 위 글의 밑줄 친 ⓐ~ⓔ 중 어법상 어색한 것을 찾아 바르게 고쳐 쓰시오.

➡ _____

**06** What difficulties did Edison have?

➡ _____
_____

# Grammar

**①** 사역동사

- Patrick **makes** me **ride** the bike. Patrick은 내가 그 자전거를 타게 한다.
- Olando **had** us **watch** his show. Olando는 우리가 그의 쇼를 관람하게 했다.

■ 사역동사는 문장의 주어가 목적어에게 어떠한 행동을 하도록 시키는 동사로 make, have, let 등이 이에 속한다.

- Kevin **made** us **come** to his party. Kevin은 우리가 그의 파티에 오게 했다.
- They **had** me **tell** about the information. 그들은 내가 그 정보에 관해 말하게 했다.
- She **let** us **play** with her toy. 그녀는 우리가 그녀의 장난감을 가지고 놀게 했다.

■ 사역동사는 5형식에 속하여 목적격 보어를 갖는데, 사역동사의 목적격 보어는 동사원형의 형태를 취하며, '~에게 …을 하게 하다'라고 해석하는 것에 유의한다.

- Molly **made** me **feel** frustrated. Molly는 내가 좌절감을 느끼게 했다.
- Jason **had** us **walk** his dog. Jason은 우리가 그의 개를 산책시키게 하였다.
- Mom **let** me **wear** her blouse. 엄마는 내가 그녀의 블라우스를 입게 하셨다.

■ 준사역동사인 help는 목적격 보어로 to부정사나 동사원형 형태를 취한다.

- Jason **helped** us **(to) solve** the problem. Jason은 우리가 그 문제를 풀게 도와주었다.

■ 목적어와 목적격 보어의 관계가 수동인 경우 사역동사 make, have는 목적격 보어로 과거분사를 쓰며, let은 목적격 보어로 'let+be p.p.' 형태를 쓴다.

- June **had** her bike **repaired** by Karl. June은 그녀의 자전거가 Karl에 의해 수리되게 했다.
- Paul **let** the wall **be painted**. Paul은 그 벽이 칠해지도록 하였다.

## 핵심 Check

1. 다음 우리말과 일치하도록 빈칸에 알맞은 말을 쓰시오.

   (1) 선생님은 우리가 서로를 돕게 하셨다.
   ➡ The teacher had _____ _____ each other.

   (2) 나는 그가 내 스마트폰을 사용하게 했다.
   ➡ I let _____ _____ my smartphone.

   (3) 그들이 요청하는 대로 되게 하여라.
   ➡ Let it be _____ as they ask.

## 2 Although

- **Although** I like skiing, I hate winter. 비록 내가 스키 타는 것을 좋아한다 해도, 나는 겨울이 싫어.
- **Though** I was not welcomed, I was happy. 비록 내가 환영받지는 못했다 해도, 나는 행복했다.

■ '비록 ~이지만[~일지라도]'라는 의미로 쓰이는 although는 양보의 부사절을 이끄는 접속사이다. 이에 해당하는 접속사로는 though, even though, while 등이 있다.

- **Although** you are in trouble, you have to stay cool. 비록 곤경에 처한다 해도, 너는 평정을 유지해야 한다.
- **While** I bought the car, I didn't drive it often. 내가 그 차를 샀다 해도, 나는 그것을 잘 몰고 다니지 않았다.
- **Though** she was my friend, she spoke ill of me.
  비록 그녀가 내 친구였다 해도, 그녀는 나에 관해 좋지 않게 말했다.

■ 양보의 부사절을 이끄는 접속사는 주절의 앞뒤에 모두 위치할 수 있으며, 주절 앞에 올 경우 콤마를 쓴다. 단, while이 양보의 의미를 나타낼 때는 주절의 앞에 위치한다.

- He pretended to be dead **though** he wasn't. 그는 죽지 않았지만 죽은 척했다.
- She followed the rule **although** she didn't think that it was a good one.
  그녀는 그것이 좋은 규칙이라고 생각하지 않았지만 그 규칙을 따랐다.
- **Although** they came late, they had dinner with us. 비록 그들이 늦게 왔다 해도, 우리와 함께 저녁을 먹었다.

■ despite(= in spite of)와 혼동하지 않도록 주의한다. despite도 '~일지라도'라는 의미를 갖지만, 전치사로 명사구를 이끈다.

- **Despite** being tired, I did what I had to do.
  = **Although** I was tired, I did what I had to do.

### 핵심 Check

**2.** 다음 우리말을 영어로 쓰시오.

(1) 비록 내가 그를 참아냈다 해도, 우리는 결국 헤어졌다.

➡ _____ I put up with him, we broke up in the end.

(2) 나는 목이 말랐지만, 물을 마시지 않았다.

➡ I didn't drink water _____ I was thirsty.

(3) 비록 그녀가 집에 일찍 왔다 해도, 우리는 그녀를 볼 수 없었다.

➡ _____ _____ she came home early, we couldn't see her.

**Grammar** 시험대비 기본평가

**01** 다음 문장에서 어법상 <u>어색한</u> 부분을 바르게 고쳐 쓰시오.

(1) He made his sister doing the dishes.

_____ ➡ _____

(2) Paul made his wife thought about the problem carefully.

_____ ➡ _____

(3) Despite I drank lots of water, I felt thirsty.

_____ ➡ _____

(4) Even she didn't invite me, I went to her party.

_____ ➡ _____

**02** 주어진 단어를 어법에 맞게 빈칸에 쓰시오.

(1) Gloria _____ together yesterday. (us / have / sing)

(2) Alicia _____ her car key the other day. (find / me / make)

(3) Mom _____ ramyeon for Dad last night. (cook / me / let)

(4) Mr. Park _____ by five. (finish / the project / have)

**03** 주어진 어구를 바르게 배열하여 다음 우리말을 영어로 쓰시오. ((1), (2), (4)는 접속사로 시작할 것.)

(1) 나는 그 집을 좋아하지만, 학교에서 너무 멀다.

(my school / it's / the house / like / too / far from / although / I)

➡ _____

(2) 나는 피곤했지만, 숙제를 했다.

(my homework / I / I / tired / was / did / though)

➡ _____

(3) 졸렸지만 Julia는 공부했다.

(sleepy / studied / Julia / was / she / although)

➡ _____

(4) 그가 나이가 많다 할지라도, 아주 힘이 세다.

(old / though / quite / he / is / he / is / strong)

➡ _____

**01** 다음 빈칸에 들어갈 말로 가장 적절한 것은?

> Jim had his sister _____ a documentary about protecting animals.

① watching ② to watch
③ watch ④ to watching
⑤ watched

**02** 다음 중 빈칸에 들어갈 말이 다른 하나는?

① _____ we woke up late, we couldn't attend the meeting.
② _____ I was listening to music, I couldn't hear what she said.
③ _____ someone stole my bag, I had to buy another one.
④ _____ she was busy, she came to visit us.
⑤ _____ she was not interested in the movie, she didn't watch it.

**03** 다음 빈칸에 들어갈 말로 적절하지 않은 것은?

> _____ they dropped by the hospital many times, they couldn't see the patient.

① Although ② Though
③ Even though ④ While
⑤ Despite

서답형
**04** 주어진 단어를 활용하여 다음 우리말을 영어로 쓰시오.

> 나는 내 차가 수리되게 했다.
> (have / fix)

➡ _____

**05** 다음 중 어법상 옳은 문장은? (2개)

① Minsu kept talking though he was told not to do so.
② She had her brother brought his note.
③ Who let you go outside?
④ Jason had the room clean.
⑤ Despite she was sad, she had to smile.

**06** 다음 빈칸에 공통으로 들어갈 말로 가장 적절한 것은?

> • She _____ me help her finish her homework.
> • They _____ us very happy.
> • I _____ them some delicious cookies.

① took ② had ③ made
④ let ⑤ got

**07** 다음 주어진 문장의 밑줄 친 부분과 같은 의미로 쓰인 것은?

> <u>While</u> I am willing to help him, he doesn't want my help.

① <u>While</u> I was talking with you, he called me.
② <u>While</u> you were having lunch, they visited your office.
③ <u>While</u> she was watering the plants, I ironed out my pants.
④ <u>While</u> you were out there, someone came to meet you in person.
⑤ <u>While</u> the sun was shining, it wasn't very warm.

**서답형**

**08** 적절한 접속사와 주어진 단어를 이용하여 다음 우리말을 영어로 쓰시오.

> 내가 강에서 수영하는 것을 좋아한다 해도, 나는 여름이 싫어. (in the river / hate)

➡ _____

 **중요**

**09** 다음 우리말을 영어로 바르게 옮기지 <u>않은</u> 것은?

① 그들은 내가 저녁을 차리게 했다.
  → They made me fix dinner.
② 비록 중요한 것은 아니었지만, 나는 그것에 관해 말하려고 노력했다.
  → I tried to talk about it although it was not important.
③ 그녀는 그가 그 의자들을 옮기게 했다.
  → She had him move the chairs.
④ 비록 우리 팀은 경기에 졌지만, 우리는 그들을 자랑스러워했다.
  → Even though our team lost the game, we were proud of our team.
⑤ 그는 건물이 파란 색으로 칠해지게 했다.
  → He had the building paint in blue.

**10** 다음 중 어법상 바르지 <u>않은</u> 것은?

> ①Even though what I ②heard yesterday, I will do ③what I want to do. My courage ④lets me ⑤follow my voice.

①          ②          ③          ④          ⑤

**서답형**

**11** 적절한 부사절 접속사를 사용하여 다음 두 문장을 하나의 문장으로 쓰시오.

> He wasn't hungry. He had dinner with her.

➡ _____

**12** 다음 빈칸에 들어갈 말로 적절하지 <u>않은</u> 것은?

> They _____ us play the game one more time.

① let          ② made          ③ had
④ helped          ⑤ wanted

 **중요**

**13** 다음 중 빈칸에 들어갈 말이 바르게 짝지어진 것은?

> • _____ her efforts, she failed.
> • Kevin had me _____ his job instead of him.

① Despite – do          ② Despite – done
③ Though – do          ④ Even though – do
⑤ In spite of – to do

**14** 다음 중 주어진 문장의 빈칸에 들어갈 말과 같은 말이 들어가는 것은?

> _____ Judy is the tallest girl in the class, she is not good at playing basketball.

① _____ I first met her, she was reading something.
② _____ he came home, he took a shower.
③ _____ I'm broke, I don't want your help any more.
④ _____ she felt sick, she went home early to take a rest.
⑤ _____ you want to succeed, do your best all the time.

**서답형**

**15** 주어진 단어를 어법에 맞게 빈칸에 쓰시오.

> Mom had the tree _____ by him. (plant)

**16** 다음 문장과 같은 의미의 문장은?

> In spite of being late, he was allowed to enter the room.

① Because of being late, he was allowed to enter the room.

② Although he was allowed to enter the room, he was late.

③ When he was late, he was allowed to enter the room.

④ He was allowed to enter the room though he was late.

⑤ Unless he was late, he was allowed to enter the room.

**17** 중요 다음 중 빈칸에 들어갈 동사의 형태가 다른 하나는?

① Jacob didn't let me _____ his computer.

② The teacher had us _____ each other.

③ She let her son _____ the car.

④ I allowed them _____ soccer after school.

⑤ Who made you _____ the windows?

서답형

**18** 주어진 어구를 바르게 배열하여 다음 우리말을 영어로 쓰시오.

> 제발 답이 무엇인지 알려 주세요.
> (know / is / let / what / please / me / the answer)

➡ _____

**19** 다음 빈칸에 들어갈 말로 가장 적절한 것은?

> She made her son _____ the bus.

① taking  ② took  ③ take
④ to taking  ⑤ taken

**20** 중요 다음 중 빈칸에 들어갈 말로 알맞지 <u>않은</u> 것은?

> _____ I was very tired, I had to finish all the work.

① Though  ② Even though
③ Although  ④ Despite
⑤ While

**21** 다음 우리말을 영어로 바르게 옮긴 것은?

> 우리는 그들이 정원에서 놀게 했다.

① We had them played in the garden.

② We help them playing in the garden.

③ We made them to play in the garden.

④ We let them play in the garden.

⑤ We let them be played in the garden.

서답형

**22** 주어진 어구를 활용하여 다음 우리말을 영어로 쓰시오.

> 그들은 내게 그 이야기 전체를 반복하게 만들었다.
> (make / repeat / the whole)

➡ _____

서답형

**23** 다음 빈칸에 알맞은 말을 쓰시오.

> _____ they are so poor, they seem happy.

서답형

**24** 다음 우리말 의미에 맞게 빈칸에 알맞은 말을 쓰시오.

> 나는 머리카락을 잘랐다.
> ➡ I had my hair _____.

**01** 적절한 부사절 접속사를 이용하여 다음 문장과 같은 의미의 문장을 쓰시오. (접속사로 시작할 것.)

> I got up early, but I was late for school.

➡ _____

**02** 다음 빈칸에 알맞은 말을 쓰시오.

| Mom made me do | |
| --- | --- |
| take care of my baby sister | ○ |
| water the flowers | × |
| brush my teeth after dinner | ○ |

(1) Mom made me _____ _____ _____ _____ _____ _____, and I did it.

(2) Mom made me _____ _____ _____, but I didn't do it.

(3) Mom made me _____ _____ _____ _____ _____, and I did it.

**03** 주어진 단어를 어법에 맞게 빈칸에 쓰시오.

(1) David helped the woman _____ the road. (cross)

(2) My mother had her wallet _____ yesterday. (steal)

(3) Who had the cheese _____? (slice)

**04** 적절한 접속사를 이용하여 다음 두 문장을 하나의 자연스러운 문장으로 쓰시오. (접속사로 시작할 것.)

> • The man hurt his leg.
> • It rained a lot.
> • Clara brought her umbrella.

> • She was wet.
> • He could walk.
> • We went to the zoo.

➡ _____

➡ _____

➡ _____

**05** 다음 대화의 빈칸에 알맞은 말을 쓰시오.

> A: What was so funny? I heard you laugh.
> B: Oh, the movie I saw was really funny. It made me _____.

**06** 주어진 말을 빈칸에 어법에 맞게 쓰시오.

> ┤ 보기 ├
>
> despite   although   even though

(1) The waiters at the restaurant were polite _____ the service was slow.

(2) _____ the great success, there is a small problem.

(3) _____ the deer ate food, they began to lose weight.

**07** 괄호 안의 단어를 어법에 맞게 바르게 배열하여 다음 시를 완성하시오.

> One Fine Day
> We (shout / people / had) "Go, Go, Tigers!"
> That (feel / made / our team / strong).
> We didn't (the other team / let / win).
> It was a fine day.

➡ _____

_____

**08** 주어진 단어를 활용하여 다음 우리말을 영어로 쓰시오.

> 비록 바람이 불었지만, 나는 축구를 하러 나갔다.
> (even though / windy / play)

➡ _____

**09** 다음 대화의 빈칸에 알맞은 말을 쓰시오.

> A: Why do you exercise in the evening?
> B: It's because my parents have _____ _____ in the evening.

**10** 다음 문장에서 어법상 틀린 것을 바르게 고쳐 쓰시오.

> Jenny let her dog running around.

➡ _____

**11** 적절한 접속사를 이용하여 다음 두 문장을 하나의 문장으로 쓰시오. (접속사로 시작할 것.)

(1) There was a heavy storm. People were safe inside.

➡ _____

(2) His throat was sore. He sang beautifully.

➡ _____

(3) She was upset. She smiled at him.

➡ _____

**12** 주어진 단어를 활용하여 다음 상황을 하나의 문장으로 요약하시오. (Peter로 시작할 것.)

> Peter wanted me to sing in front of people. But I didn't want to do it. He kept saying that I should do it, so I sang in front of people. (make)

➡ _____

_____

**13** 주어진 단어를 어법에 맞게 빈칸에 쓰시오.

(1) I had my clothes _____ by him. (wash)

(2) My mom made my little sister _____ care of by my brother. (take)

(3) We let the book _____ _____ by other students. (read)

(4) I had my report _____ by my best friend. (review)

## Playing Soccer on the Water

Koh Panyee was a small floating village in the middle of the sea.
~의 가운데에

Although the boys in the village never played soccer before, they loved
양보절 접속사(비록 ~일지라도)

watching it on TV. One day, the boys decided to make their own soccer
= to watch   = soccer                    to부정사를 목적어로 취하는 동사

team. However, people laughed at their idea.
      그러나          ~을 비웃다

"That's impossible."
축구팀을 만든다는 것

"What makes you say so?"
      사역동사+목적어+동사원형

"Look around. Where are you going to play soccer?"

The villagers were right. The boys had no place to play soccer. They
                                          to부정사의 형용사적 용법(place 수식)

were discouraged.
낙담을 느꼈으므로 과거분사

"Don't give up! We can still play soccer."
                      아직도, 여전히

"How?"

"Let's make our own soccer field."
          우리들 자신의

The boys gathered old boats and pieces of wood. They put the boats
                                                    put A together: A를 합치다

together and nailed the wood to them. After much hard work, they
                        the boats        불가산 명사 work 수식

finally had a floating field. It was shaky and had nails everywhere. The
                          = The floating field

ball and the boys would often fall into the sea, so the field was always
              ~하곤 했다(과거의 습관) 빈도부사(일반동사 앞, be동사나 조동사 뒤에 위치)

wet and slippery.

---

floating 떠 있는
village 마을
middle 중앙, 가운데
although 비록 ~일지라도
decide 결정하다
own 자신의
laugh at 비웃다
impossible 불가능한
villager 마을 사람
discouraged 낙담한
give up 포기하다
field 운동장, 들판
gather 모으다
nail 못을 박다
shaky 흔들거리는, 휘청거리는
everywhere 어디에나

---

📎 **확인문제**

● 다음 문장이 본문의 내용과 일치하면 T, 일치하지 않으면 F를 쓰시오.

1  Koh Panyee was a small village floating on the water. ☐

2  The boys in Koh Panyee played often soccer on the ground. ☐

3  A soccer team was made by the boys. ☐

4  People thought that the boys could make their own soccer team. ☐

5  The boys made their own soccer field out of old boats and pieces of wood. ☐

They had no shoes so they had to play in bare feet. Still, they didn't
　　　　　　　　　　　　　　　　　　맨발　　그럼에도 불구하고
care. In fact, they built excellent skills and enjoyed playing soccer
　　　　　　　　　　　　　　　　　　　　　동명사를 목적어로 취하는 동사
more.

　One day, a boy brought a poster about a soccer tournament. They
　어느 날
decided to give it a try. When they were about to leave, the villagers
　　　　시도해 보다　　　　　　　be about to V: 막 V하려고 하다
gave them new shoes and uniforms. Some even came to watch the
4형식 동사(give+사람+사물)　　　　　　　= Some villagers
game. This made the boys feel better. At first, people saw them as the
몇몇 마을 사람들이 경기를 보러 온 것　　　동사 원형　　　처음에　　　　　～으로(자격)
weakest team. However, when the tournament started, the soccer team
surprised everyone.

　On the day of the semi-final, it was raining hard. They were losing by
특정한 날 앞에 전치사 on　　　　　　　비인칭 주어　　　　　　　차이를 나타내는 전치사 (두 골 차이로)
two goals and it looked impossible to win.
　　　　　　　가주어　　　　　　진주어
　"The other team is so strong," they thought.

But the boys didn't give up. They took off their shoes during the
　　　　　　　　　　　　　　　　　　　　　　　～ 동안
second half and the game changed completely. They played better in
the rain thanks to the slippery field at home. Although they lost by a
　　　　　～ 덕분에
score of three to two, still, they felt proud of themselves. They didn't
　　　　　3대 2　　　　　　　　　　　주어와 목적어가 같으므로 재귀대명사 (재귀적 용법)
give up when they were losing. They tried their best until the end.
　　　　　　　　　　　　　　　try one's best: 최선을 다하다　　끝까지

fall into ~에 빠지다
slippery 미끄러운
bare 벌거벗은, 맨 ~
in fact 사실상
tournament 토너먼트
semi-final 준결승
take off 벗다
completely 완전히
proud 자랑스러운
until ~까지

### 확인문제

● 다음 문장이 본문의 내용과 일치하면 T, 일치하지 않으면 F를 쓰시오.

1　Although boys played in bare feet, they enjoyed playing soccer. ☐

2　One of adults in the village brought a poster about a soccer tournament. ☐

3　The villagers didn't care that the boys took part in the soccer game. ☐

4　The boys didn't wear their shoes during the second half. ☐

5　The boys did their best. ☐

● 우리말을 참고하여 빈칸에 알맞은 말을 쓰시오.

**1** Koh Panyee was a small _____ _____ in the _____ of the sea.

**2** _____ the boys in the village _____ _____ _____ before, they loved _____ _____ on TV.

**3** One day, the boys _____ _____ _____ their own soccer team.

**4** _____, people _____ _____ their idea.

**5** "That's _____."

**6** "What _____ you _____ _____?"

**7** "_____ _____. Where are you going _____ _____ soccer?"

**8** The villagers _____ _____. The boys had no place _____ _____ _____.

**9** They were _____.

**10** "Don't _____ _____! We can _____ _____ _____."

**11** "_____?"

**12** "Let's _____ _____ _____ soccer field."

**13** The boys _____ old boats and _____ _____ wood.

**14** They _____ the boats _____ and _____ the wood _____ them.

**15** _____ _____ hard work, they finally _____ _____ _____.

**16** It was _____ and had _____ everywhere.

---

**1** Koh Panyee는 바다 가운데 떠 있는 작은 수상 마을이었다.

**2** 비록 그 마을의 소년들은 이전에 축구를 해 본 적이 없었지만, 그들은 그것을 TV로 보는 것을 정말 좋아했다.

**3** 어느 날, 그 소년들은 그들만의 축구팀을 만들기로 하였다.

**4** 그러나 사람들은 그들의 생각을 비웃었다.

**5** "그것은 불가능해."

**6** "왜 그렇게 말하는 거죠?"

**7** "주위를 둘러봐. 너희는 어디서 축구를 할 거니?"

**8** 마을 사람들이 옳았다. 소년들은 축구를 할 장소가 없었다.

**9** 그들은 낙담했다.

**10** "포기하지 마! 우리는 여전히 축구를 할 수 있어."

**11** "어떻게?"

**12** "우리만의 축구장을 만들자."

**13** 소년들은 낡은 배와 나뭇조각들을 모았다.

**14** 그들은 배를 합치고 그것들 위에 나무를 못으로 박았다.

**15** 매우 열심히 일한 후, 그들은 마침내 떠 있는 축구장을 가지게 되었다.

**16** 그것은 흔들리고 곳곳에 못이 있었다.

17 The ball and the boys _____ _____ _____ _____ the sea, so the field was always _____ and _____.

18 They had _____ _____ so they had to play in _____ _____.

19 Still, _____ didn't _____.

20 _____ _____, they built _____ skills and _____ playing soccer more.

21 One day, a boy _____ _____ _____ about a soccer tournament.

22 They _____ _____ give _____ a try.

23 _____ they _____ _____ _____ _____ _____, the villagers gave _____ new shoes and uniforms.

24 Some even came to watch the game. This _____ the boys _____ better.

25 At first, people _____ them _____ the _____ team.

26 _____, when the tournament _____, the soccer team _____ everyone.

27 _____ the day of the semi-final, it _____ _____ _____.

28 They were _____ _____ _____ _____ and it looked _____ _____ _____.

29 "_____ _____ team is _____ _____," they thought.

30 But the boys didn't _____ _____.

31 They _____ _____ their shoes _____ the second half and the game _____ _____.

32 They _____ _____ in the rain thanks to the slippery field at home.

33 Although they _____ _____ a score of three _____ two, still, they felt _____ _____ _____.

34 They didn't give up _____ _____ _____ _____. They _____ _____ _____ until the end.

17 공과 소년들은 종종 바다에 빠졌고, 축구장은 항상 젖어 있고 미끄러웠다.

18 그들은 신발이 없어서 맨발로 축구를 해야 했다.

19 그런데도 그들은 상관하지 않았다.

20 실제로 그들은 훌륭한 기술을 쌓고 더욱 더 축구를 즐겼다.

21 어느 날, 한 소년이 축구 토너먼트에 관한 포스터를 가지고 왔다.

22 그들은 한번 해 보기로 결정했다.

23 그들이 떠나려고 할 때, 마을 사람들은 그들에게 새 신발과 축구복을 주었다.

24 몇몇은 심지어 경기를 보러 왔다. 이것은 소년들의 기분을 더 좋게 만들었다.

25 처음에, 사람들은 그들을 가장 약한 팀으로 보았다.

26 그러나 토너먼트가 시작되었을 때, 그 축구팀은 모든 사람들을 놀라게 했다.

27 준결승전 날, 비가 심하게 오고 있었다.

28 그들은 두 골 차로 지고 있었고, 이기는 것은 불가능해 보였다.

29 "다른 팀이 아주 강해."라고 그들은 생각했다.

30 그러나 소년들은 포기하지 않았다.

31 그들은 후반전에 그들의 신발을 벗었고 경기는 완전히 바뀌었다.

32 고향의 미끄러운 축구장 덕분에 그들은 빗속에서 더 잘하였다.

33 비록 그들은 3대 2로 졌지만, 그들은 그들 자신이 자랑스러웠다.

34 그들은 그들이 지고 있을 때 포기하지 않았다. 그들은 끝까지 최선을 다하였다.

● 우리말을 참고하여 본문을 영작하시오.

**1** ▸ Koh Panyee는 바다 가운데 떠 있는 작은 수상 마을이었다.

➡ _____

**2** ▸ 비록 그 마을의 소년들은 이전에 축구를 해 본 적이 없었지만, 그들은 그것을 TV로 보는 것을 정말 좋아했다.

➡ _____

**3** ▸ 어느 날, 그 소년들은 그들만의 축구팀을 만들기로 하였다.

➡ _____

**4** ▸ 그러나 사람들은 그들의 생각을 비웃었다.

➡ _____

**5** ▸ "그것은 불가능해."

➡ _____

**6** ▸ "왜 그렇게 말하는 거죠?"

➡ _____

**7** ▸ "주위를 둘러봐. 너희는 어디서 축구를 할 거니?"

➡ _____

**8** ▸ 마을 사람들이 옳았다. 소년들은 축구를 할 장소가 없었다.

➡ _____

**9** ▸ 그들은 낙담했다.

➡ _____

**10** ▸ "포기하지 마! 우리는 여전히 축구를 할 수 있어."

➡ _____

**11** ▸ "어떻게?"

➡ _____

**12** ▸ "우리만의 축구장을 만들자."

➡ _____

**13** ▸ 소년들은 낡은 배와 나뭇조각들을 모았다.

➡ _____

**14** ▸ 그들은 배를 합치고 그것들 위에 나무를 못으로 박았다.

➡ _____

**15** ▸ 매우 열심히 일한 후, 그들은 마침내 떠 있는 축구장을 가지게 되었다.

➡ _____

**16** ▸ 그것은 흔들리고 곳곳에 못이 있었다.

➡ _____

**17** 공과 소년들은 종종 바다에 빠졌고, 축구장은 항상 젖어 있고 미끄러웠다.

　➡ _____

**18** 그들은 신발이 없어서 맨발로 축구를 해야 했다.

　➡ _____

**19** 그런데도 그들은 상관하지 않았다.

　➡ _____

**20** 실제로 그들은 훌륭한 기술을 쌓았고 더욱 더 축구를 즐겼다.

　➡ _____

**21** 어느 날, 한 소년이 축구 토너먼트에 관한 포스터를 가지고 왔다.

　➡ _____

**22** 그들은 한번 해 보기로 결정했다.

　➡ _____

**23** 그들이 떠나려고 할 때, 마을 사람들은 그들에게 새 신발과 축구복을 주었다.

　➡ _____

**24** 몇몇은 심지어 경기를 보러 왔다. 이것은 소년들의 기분을 더 좋게 만들었다.

　➡ _____

**25** 처음에, 사람들은 그들을 가장 약한 팀으로 보았다.

　➡ _____

**26** 그러나 토너먼트가 시작되었을 때, 그 축구팀은 모든 사람들을 놀라게 했다.

　➡ _____

**27** 준결승전 날, 비가 심하게 오고 있었다.

　➡ _____

**28** 그들은 두 골 차로 지고 있었고, 이기는 것은 불가능해 보였다.

　➡ _____

**29** "다른 팀이 아주 강해."라고 그들은 생각했다.

　➡ _____

**30** 그러나 소년들은 포기하지 않았다.

　➡ _____

**31** 그들은 후반전에 그들의 신발을 벗었고 경기는 완전히 바뀌었다.

　➡ _____

**32** 고향의 미끄러운 축구장 덕분에 그들은 빗속에서 더 잘하였다.

　➡ _____

**33** 비록 그들은 3대 2로 졌지만, 그들은 그들 자신이 자랑스러웠다.

　➡ _____

**34** 그들은 그들이 지고 있을 때 포기하지 않았다. 그들은 끝까지 최선을 다하였다.

　➡ _____

[01~03] 다음 글을 읽고 물음에 답하시오.

Koh Panyee was a small ___(A)___ village in the middle of the sea. Although the boys in the village never played soccer before, they loved watching it on TV. One day, the boys decided to make their own soccer team. ___(B)___, people laughed at their idea.
"That's impossible."
"What makes you say so?"
"Look around. Where are you going to play soccer?"
The villagers were right. The boys had no place to play soccer. They were discouraged.
"Don't give up! We can still play soccer."
"How?"
"Let's make our own soccer field."

**서답형**

**01** 단어 float을 어법에 맞게 빈칸 (A)에 쓰시오.

➡ _____

**02** 다음 중 빈칸 (B)에 들어갈 말로 적절한 것은?

① In addition          ② Besides
③ However             ④ As a result
⑤ For example

**03** 다음 중 위 글의 내용과 일치하는 것은?

① Koh Panyee is located in the middle of the island.
② The boys in the village often played soccer.
③ People in the village thought it was possible to make a soccer team.
④ The boys gave up making their own soccer team.
⑤ The boys enjoyed watching soccer on TV.

[04~07] 다음 글을 읽고 물음에 답하시오.

The boys gathered old boats and pieces of wood. ①They put the boats together and nailed the wood to ②them. After much hard work, they finally had (A)a floating field. It was shaky and had nails everywhere. The ball and the boys would often fall into the sea, so the field was always wet and slippery. ③They had no shoes so ④they had to play in bare feet. Still, they didn't care. In fact, ⑤ they built excellent skills and enjoyed (B) play soccer more.

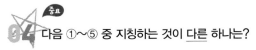

**04** 다음 ①~⑤ 중 지칭하는 것이 다른 하나는?

①          ②          ③          ④          ⑤

**05** 다음 중 밑줄 친 (A)에 대한 설명으로 바르지 않은 것은?

① It was made by the boys who wanted to play soccer on it.
② It was made up of old boats and pieces of wood.
③ It had so many nails everywhere.
④ It was not stable.
⑤ It was floating in the air.

**서답형**

**06** 다음과 같이 풀이되는 말을 위 글에서 찾아 쓰시오.

difficult to stand on, move on, or hold because of being smooth, wet, icy, etc.

➡ _____

**서답형**

**07** 밑줄 친 (B)를 어법에 맞게 고쳐 쓰시오.

➡ _____

[08~12] 다음 글을 읽고 물음에 답하시오.

One day, a boy brought a poster about a soccer tournament. ① They decided to give it a try. When they were about to leave, the villagers gave them new shoes and uniforms. Some even came to watch the game. ② At first, people saw them as the weakest team. ③ However, when the tournament started, the soccer team surprised everyone.

On the day of the semi-final, it was raining (A)hard. ④ They were losing by two goals and it looked impossible to win. ⑤

"The other team is so strong," they thought. But the boys didn't give up. They took off their shoes during the second half and the game changed completely. They played better in the rain (B)thanks to the slippery field at home. Although they lost by a score of three to two, still, they felt proud of themselves. They didn't give up when they were losing. They tried their best until the end.

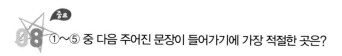

**08** ①~⑤ 중 다음 주어진 문장이 들어가기에 가장 적절한 곳은?

This made the boys feel better.

①     ②     ③     ④     ⑤

**09** 다음 중 밑줄 친 (A)와 같은 의미로 쓰인 것은?

① It's hard to learn a foreign language.
② I've had a long hard day.
③ The bread is hard to chew.
④ It was snowing hard then.
⑤ She is a very hard worker.

**10** 다음 중 밑줄 친 (B)를 대신하여 쓸 수 있는 것은?

① despite        ② beside
③ due to        ④ according to
⑤ as well as

**11** 다음 중 위 글을 읽고 답할 수 없는 것은?

① What was the poster about?
② Who gave the boys new shoes and uniforms?
③ What did the boys do during the second half?
④ Why did the boys play better in the rain?
⑤ How many games did the boys play?

서답형
**12** 위 글의 내용에 맞게 빈칸에 알맞은 말을 쓰시오.

_____ the boys thought the other team was very strong, they didn't _____ _____.

[13~15] 다음 글을 읽고 물음에 답하시오.

My ①favorite sport is basketball. However, I wasn't really good at it ②at first. I couldn't shoot well unlike other players. Although I felt ③encouraged, I didn't ④give up. I practiced shooting for an hour every day. (A)This made me (B)to shoot well. Now, I'm ⑤ the best player on our team.

**13** 다음 ①~⑤ 중 글의 흐름상 어색한 것은?

①     ②     ③     ④     ⑤

**서답형**

**14** 밑줄 친 (A)가 의미하는 것을 우리말로 쓰시오.

➡ _____

**서답형**

**15** 밑줄 친 (B)를 어법에 맞게 고쳐 쓰시오.

➡ _____

[16~19] 다음 글을 읽고 물음에 답하시오.

Koh Panyee was a small floating village in the middle of the sea. Although the boys in the village never played soccer before, they loved watching it on TV. One day, the boys decided to make their own soccer team. However, people laughed ___(A)___ their idea.

"That's impossible."

"What makes you say so?"

"Look around. Where are you going to play soccer?"

The villagers were right. The boys had no place to play soccer. They were ___(B)___.

**16** 다음 중 빈칸 (A)에 들어갈 말과 같은 말이 들어가는 것은?

① Please take good care _____ your baby brother, Tommy.

② They are not interested _____ making something from clay.

③ I don't want you to give _____ your dream.

④ They are looking forward _____ visiting the museum.

⑤ Simon jumped up and down because he was pleased _____ the news.

**17** 다음 중 빈칸 (B)에 들어갈 말로 가장 적절한 것은?

① thankful    ② delighted    ③ bored
④ surprised    ⑤ discouraged

**서답형**

**18** What did the boys decide to do? Answer in English with a full sentence.

➡ _____

**중요**

**19** 다음 중 위 글의 내용과 일치하는 것은?

① People in the village supported the boys' idea.

② There was a soccer field in Koh Panyee.

③ There was no TV in the village.

④ The boys had much experience of playing soccer.

⑤ The village was in the middle of the sea.

[20~22] 다음 글을 읽고 물음에 답하시오.

"Don't give up! We can still play soccer."

"How?"

"Let's make our own soccer field."

The boys gathered old boats and pieces of wood. They put the boats together and nailed the wood to them. After much hard work, they finally had a floating field. It was shaky and had nails everywhere. The ball and the boys would often fall into the sea, so the field was always wet and slippery. They had no shoes so they had to play in bare feet. Still, they didn't care. In fact, they built excellent skills and enjoyed playing soccer more.

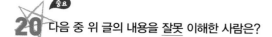
**20** 다음 중 위 글의 내용을 잘못 이해한 사람은?

① James: It must be really hard to make a floating field.

② Kevin: I really respect the boy's will.

③ Jim: I can't imagine playing soccer without wearing shoes. It must be really difficult.

④ Penny: I think their floating field was not safe enough to play soccer because of the nails.

⑤ Peter: The soccer field must be very steady and stable.

서답형

**21** 위 글의 내용에 맞게 다음 빈칸에 알맞은 말을 쓰시오.

> _____ there were many difficulties, the boys didn't care and _____ _____ _____, enjoying playing soccer more.

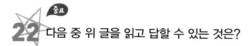
**22** 다음 중 위 글을 읽고 답할 수 있는 것은?

① How many boats were needed to make the soccer field?

② From where did the boys bring the boats and pieces of wood?

③ When did the boys usually play soccer?

④ How many boys gathered to make the soccer field?

⑤ Who nailed the wood to the old boats?

[23~26] 다음 글을 읽고 물음에 답하시오.

> One day, a boy brought a poster about a soccer tournament. They decided (A)to give it a try. When they were about ①to leave, the villagers gave them new shoes and uniforms. Some even came ②to watch the game. This

made the boys ③feel better. At first, people saw them as the weakest team. However, when the tournament started, the soccer team surprised everyone.

On the day of the semi-final, it was raining hard. They were losing by two goals and it looked impossible ④to win.

"The other team is so strong," they thought.

But the boys didn't give up. They took off their shoes during the second half and the game changed completely. They played better in the rain thanks to the slippery field at home. Although they lost by a score of three to two, still, they felt proud of ⑤them. They didn't give up when they were losing. They tried their best until the end.

**23** 밑줄 친 (A)의 의미로 가장 적절한 것은?

① to make a poster about the soccer team

② to take part in the tournament

③ to use it for making a soccer field

④ to try hard to take part in the show

⑤ to gather more boys to play soccer with

서답형

**24** What did the villagers give to the boys? Answer in English with a full sentence.

➡ _____

서답형

**25** How was the weather on the day of the semi-final?

➡ _____

**26** ①~⑤ 중 어법상 바르지 않은 것은?

① ② ③ ④ ⑤

**[01~03]** 다음 글을 읽고 물음에 답하시오.

Koh Panyee was a small floating village in the middle of the sea. Although the boys in the village never played soccer before, they loved watching it on TV. One day, the boys decided to make their own soccer team. However, people laughed at their idea.

"(A)That's impossible."

"What makes you say so?"

"Look around. Where are you going to play soccer?"

The villagers were right. The boys had no place to play soccer. They were discouraged.

"Don't give up! We can still play soccer."

"How?"

"Let's make our own soccer field."

**01** 밑줄 친 (A)가 의미하는 것을 위 글에서 찾아 영어로 쓰시오.

➡ _____

**02** Where is Koh Panyee? Answer in English with a full sentence.

➡ _____

**03** 위 글의 내용에 맞게 빈칸에 알맞은 말을 쓰시오.

> The boys living in a small village called _____ loved to watch soccer but they had no experience of _____ _____. So, they decided to _____ _____ soccer team _____ difficult conditions.

**[04~07]** 다음 글을 읽고 물음에 답하시오.

The boys gathered old boats and pieces of wood. They put the boats together and nailed the wood to them. After much hard work, they finally had a floating field. (A)It was shaky and had nails everywhere. The ball and the boys would often fall into the sea, so the field was always wet and slippery. They had no shoes so they had to play in bare feet. Still, they didn't care. In fact, they built excellent skills and enjoyed playing soccer more.

**04** Write the reason why the field was always wet and slippery. Use the phrase 'It's because.'

➡ _____
_____

**05** What did the boys gather to make their own soccer field? Answer in English with a full sentence.

➡ _____

**06** 밑줄 친 (A)가 가리키는 것을 위 글에서 찾아 쓰시오.

➡ _____

**07** 위 글의 표현을 이용하여 다음 우리말을 영어로 쓰시오.

> 비록 신발이 없다 할지라도, 우리는 신경 쓰지 않았어.

➡ _____

[08~12] 다음 글을 읽고 물음에 답하시오.

One day, a boy brought a poster about a soccer tournament. They decided to give it a try. When they were about to leave, the villagers gave them new shoes and uniforms. Some even came to watch the game. This made the boys feel better. At first, people saw them as the weakest team. However, when the tournament started, the soccer team surprised everyone.

On the day of the semi-final, it was raining hard. They were losing by two goals and (A) 이기는 것은 불가능해 보였다.

"The other team is so strong," they thought.

But the boys didn't give up. They took off their shoes during the second half and the game changed completely. They played better in the rain thanks to the slippery field at home.  ⓐ  they lost by a score of three to two, still, they felt proud of themselves. They didn't give up when they were losing. They tried their best until the end.

**08** 빈칸 ⓐ에 알맞은 접속사를 쓰시오.

➡ _____

**09** What did a boy bring? Answer in English with a full sentence.

➡ _____

**10** 주어진 단어를 활용하여 밑줄 친 우리말 (A)를 영어로 쓰시오.

| (it / look) |
| --- |

➡ _____

**11** What did the boys do during the second half?

➡ _____

**12** 위 글의 내용에 맞게 빈칸에 알맞은 말을 쓰시오.

| Because of the slippery field at home, they _____ _____ _____ _____ _____. |
| --- |

[13~15] 다음 글을 읽고 물음에 답하시오.

**Dear Koh Panyee Soccer Team**

Hello, I became ①your fan after watching one of your matches. Everyone thought you ②would lose because the other team was ③weak. But you didn't give up. During the second half, I was surprised to see you play in bare feet. You were playing ④better than before! I guess playing soccer on a field in the sea helped you a lot. Although you ⑤lost by a score of three to two, I became a fan of your team. Hope to see you soon.

Yours,
Fern Yahtie

**13** ①~⑤ 중 글의 흐름상 어색한 것을 바르게 고쳐 쓰시오.

➡ _____ ➡ _____

**14** What made Fern surprised? Answer in English with a full sentence.

➡ _____

**15** 글의 내용에 맞게 빈칸에 알맞은 말을 쓰시오.

| Watching one of Koh Panyee soccer team's matches made Fern Yahtie _____ _____ _____. |
| --- |

해석

## Real Life Communication - Step 2

A: I want to be a basketball player but I'm too short. Should I give up?
to부정사의 명사적 용법(목적어)    너무

B: No, don't give up! Have you heard of Anthony Webb?
격려하기        have+p.p: 현재 완료

A: No, I haven't. Who is he?
don't(x)

B: He was a basketball player. He was short, but he won the 1986 Slam Dunk

Contest.

구문해설 • give up: 포기하다

A: 나는 농구 선수가 되고 싶어. 근데 나는 키가 너무 작아. 내가 포기해야 할까?
B: 아니, 포기하지 마! Anthony Webb에 대해 들어 봤니?
A: 아니, 그가 누군데?
B: 그는 농구선수였어. 그는 키가 작았지만, 1986 Slam Dunk Contest 에서 우승했어.

## Culture & Life

The women's field hockey team from Zimbabwe surprised the whole world.
출신을 나타내는 전치사

Although they had only a month to prepare, they won the gold medal at the
양보의 부사절 접속사            to부정사의 형용사적 용법

1980 Olympic Games.

구문해설 • surprise: ~을 놀라게 하다  • whole: 전체의  • although: 비록 ~일지라도
• prepare: 준비하다

짐바브웨 여자 필드하키 팀은 전 세계를 놀라게 했다. 비록 그들은 준비할 시간이 한 달 밖에 없었지만, 그들은 1980년 올림픽 게임에서 금메달을 땄다.

## Let's Write

My favorite sport is basketball. However, I wasn't really good at it at first. I
basketball 지칭

couldn't shoot well unlike other players. Although I felt discouraged, I didn't
전치사(~와 달리)                감정을 느낄 때 쓰는 과거분사

give up. I practiced shooting for an hour every day. This made me shoot well.
동명사를 목적어로 취하는 동사            사역동사+목적어+동사원형

Now, I'm the best player on our team.

구문해설 • favorite: 가장 좋아하는  • unlike: ~와 달리  • discouraged: 낙담한
• practice: 연습하다

내가 가장 좋아하는 운동은 농구이다. 그러나 처음에 나는 농구를 잘하지 못했다. 나는 다른 선수들과 달리 슛을 잘하지 못했다. 나는 낙담했지만, 포기하지 않았다. 나는 매일 한 시간 동안 슛 연습을 했다. 이것이 내가 슛을 잘하게 했다. 이제, 나는 우리 팀에서 가장 잘하는 선수이다.

**01** 다음 짝지어진 단어의 관계가 같도록 빈칸에 알맞은 말을 쓰시오.

> patient : impatient = possible : _____

**02** 다음 영영풀이가 가리키는 것을 고르시오.

> to kick or throw a ball in a sport such as football or basketball towards the place where you can get a point

① shoot  ② shout  ③ gather
④ decide  ⑤ match

**03** 다음 중 밑줄 친 부분의 뜻풀이가 바르지 <u>않은</u> 것은?

① The floor was <u>slippery</u>, so be careful. 미끄러운
② The rugby <u>field</u> was wet after the rain. …장
③ It's <u>impossible</u> to get back home in time for dinner. 불가능한
④ All the <u>villagers</u> got together to celebrate the New Year. 마을
⑤ I want to have my <u>own</u> room. 자신의

**04** 다음 우리말에 맞게 빈칸을 완성하시오.

(1) 오늘 우리는 강한 팀에 맞서 큰 경기를 했다.
  ➡ Today, we had a big match _____ a strong team.
(2) 비록 비가 내리고 있었지만, 나는 축구를 했다.
  ➡ _____ it was raining, I played soccer.
(3) 그들은 맨발로 뛰지만 행복하다.
  ➡ They play in _____ feet but they're happy.
(4) 그럼에도 그들은 그들 자신이 자랑스러웠다.
  ➡ _____, they felt proud of themselves.

**05** 다음 주어진 문장의 밑줄 친 <u>match</u>와 같은 의미로 쓰인 것은?

> Are you looking forward to your tennis <u>match</u> tomorrow?

① The <u>match</u> ended in a victory for my team.
② The curtains and carpet are a good <u>match</u>.
③ Jimmy and Emma are a perfect <u>match</u> for each other.
④ Would you give me a box of <u>matches</u>?
⑤ The little girl stroke the last <u>match</u>.

**06** 다음 문장에 공통으로 들어갈 말을 고르시오.

> • Stop biting your _____s. It's not good for your health.
> • She caught her sweater on a _____.
> • Would you _____ up the door for me?

① nail  ② shoot
③ bat  ④ match
⑤ meal

**07** 다음 우리말과 일치하도록 주어진 단어를 모두 배열하여 영작하시오.

(1) 나는 마라톤 경주 후에 내 자신이 자랑스러웠다.
  (proud / the / marathon / after / race / felt / I / of / myself)
  ➡ _____
(2) 그녀는 맨발로 숲을 걸었다.
  (bare / she / the / in / woods / feet / walked / in)
  ➡ _____
(3) 지더라도 낙담하지 마라.
  (be / you / even / lose / if / don't / discouraged)
  ➡ _____

**Conversation**

[08~10] 다음 대화를 읽고 물음에 답하시오.

> Father: Emily, are you ⓐexcited about your match on Saturday?
>
> Emily: Not really. We're playing against a strong team. I think we'll lose.
>
> Father: Don't say ⓑthat. Have you heard about the Greek team in the 2004 Euro Cup?
>
> Emily: No, I ⓒdidn't. What about them?
>
> Father: They were a weak team, so everyone thought ⓓthat they would lose.
>
> Emily: What happened?
>
> Father: They played as a team and ⓔworked hard. Finally, they won the Euro Cup. So, _____(A)_____.
>
> Emily: Thanks, Dad. We'll try our best.

**08** 위 대화의 밑줄 친 ⓐ~ⓔ 중 어법상 어색한 것을 찾아 바르게 고치시오.

➡ _____

**09** 위 대화의 빈칸 (A)에 들어갈 말로 어색한 것은?

① don't give up
② cheer up
③ believe you can do it
④ try your best
⑤ try next time

**10** 위 대화의 내용과 일치하지 않는 것은?

① Emily는 토요일에 경기가 있다.
② Emily는 강한 팀에 맞서 시합을 할 것이다.
③ 2004 유로컵에서 그리스 팀은 약한 팀이었다.
④ 2004 유로컵에서 그리스 팀은 한 팀으로 경기하며 열심히 노력하였다.
⑤ 2004 유로컵에서 그리스 팀은 준우승하였다.

[11~12] 다음 대화를 읽고 물음에 답하시오.

> Sora: Alex, have you heard about this year's "Ugly Sweater Party?"
>
> Alex: Of course, I have. It's on December 5th, right?
>
> Sora: That's right. Are you going to go?
>
> Alex: I want to, but I don't have an ugly sweater.
>
> Sora: I have one that I don't wear at home. You can have it if you want.
>
> Alex: Thanks. That would be great.
>
> Sora: Let's meet in front of the Student Center and go inside together.
>
> Alex: Sure. See you then.

**11** When will this year's "Ugly Sweater Party" be held?

➡ _____

**12** Where will Sora and Alex meet?

➡ _____

**13** 다음 대화가 자연스럽게 이어지도록 순서대로 배열하시오.

> Suji: Hojun, are you going to try out for the school ice hockey team? The new season is about to start.

> (A) Okay, I'll try my best. Thanks a lot.
> (B) Why not?
> (C) I'm not sure.
> (D) Well, you're also good at ice hockey, so don't give up!
> (E) I heard that Tony and Brad are also trying out for the team. They're so good.

➡ _____

**14** 다음 짝지어진 대화가 <u>어색한</u> 것은?

① A: Have you heard of Sepak Takraw?
　B: No, I haven't. What is it?

② A: Have you heard of cricket?
　B: Of course I have.

③ A: I'd like to play soccer well, but it's not easy.
　B: Don't give up. Why don't you practice every day after school?

④ A: I want to be a basketball player but I'm too short. Should I give up?
　B: No, don't give up!

⑤ A: I want to be a baseball player but I'm not good at it. What should I do?
　B: I'll do my best to be a good player.

**Grammar**

**15** 다음 빈칸에 들어갈 말로 가장 적절한 것은?

> She didn't make me _____ out late at night.

① staying　　② to stay　　③ stay
④ to staying　　⑤ stayed

**16** 다음 중 빈칸에 들어갈 말이 <u>다른</u> 하나는?

① I did it _____ he told me to.

② We didn't tell you _____ we knew that it would hurt you.

③ _____ we are here, we are going to visit the most famous museum in this area.

④ Anne was fond of Tom _____ he often annoyed her.

⑤ Orlando ordered much food _____ he was hungry.

**17** 주어진 문장과 같은 의미의 문장은?

> I had him carry my heavy bag.

① I made him to carry my heavy bag.
② I let him carrying my heavy bag.
③ I wanted him carry my heavy bag.
④ I had my heavy bag carried by him.
⑤ I helped him to carry my heavy bag.

**18** 적절한 접속사로 시작하여 다음 두 문장을 하나의 문장으로 쓰시오.

> I was tired. I studied hard in class.

➡ _____

**19** 다음 중 어법상 올바른 문장은?

① She got Jim walk the dog.
② I made her to wash dishes.
③ Despite she didn't like it, she pretended to like it.
④ Who let you play the guitar?
⑤ In spite the rain, he went to school by bicycle.

**20** 다음 중 빈칸에 들어갈 말로 알맞지 <u>않은</u> 것은?

> My mom _____ me clean the floor.

① had　　② made　　③ helped
④ let　　⑤ got

**21** 다음 우리말에 맞게 빈칸에 알맞은 말을 쓰시오.

> 비록 그는 일찍 떠났지만, 비행기를 놓쳤다.
> ➡ _____ _____ _____ _____
>   though _____ _____ _____.

**22** 다음 빈칸에 들어갈 말로 적절한 것을 모두 고르시오.

> My cousin helped me _____ into my new apartment.

① move
② moving
③ to move
④ to moving
⑤ moved

**23** 다음 중 빈칸에 들어갈 말이 바르게 짝지어진 것은?

> • _____ the weather was cold, I went swimming.
> • _____ me go shopping with my friends.

① Despite – Let
② Even though – Let's
③ Although – Allow
④ Even though – Let
⑤ Although – Get

**24** 다음 빈칸에 알맞은 말을 쓰시오.

> 비록 네가 말을 물가로 끌고 갈 수는 있더라도, 말이 물을 마시게 할 수는 없다.
> ➡ _____ you can lead a horse to water, you can't make him _____ it.

**25** 주어진 단어를 활용하여 다음 우리말을 8단어로 이루어진 한 문장의 영어로 쓰시오.

> 나의 부모님은 내가 폭력적인 영화를 보게 하지 않으신다.
> (let / violent movies)

➡ _____

Reading

**[26~28]** 다음 글을 읽고 물음에 답하시오.

> Koh Panyee was a small floating village in the middle of the sea. Although the boys in the village never played soccer before, they loved watching it on TV. One day, the boys decided to make their own soccer team. However, people laughed at their idea.
> "That's impossible."
> "ⓐWhat makes you to say so?"
> "Look around. _____(A)_____"
> The villagers were right. The boys had no place to play soccer. They were discouraged.
> "Don't give up! We can still play soccer."
> "How?"
> "Let's make our own soccer field."

**26** 다음 중 빈칸 (A)에 들어갈 말로 가장 적절한 것은?

① Who are you going to play with?
② What do you want to do?
③ Why do you want to do that?
④ Where are you going to play soccer?
⑤ Who is going to teach you how to play soccer?

**27** 밑줄 친 ⓐ에서 어법상 틀린 것을 바르게 고쳐 문장을 다시 쓰시오.

➡ _____

## 28 위 글에 이어질 내용으로 적절한 것은?

① the boys who are trying to see soccer on TV

② the reason why the boys live in the village

③ the boys who are trying to make their soccer field

④ how to play soccer in the water

⑤ the reason why people laughed at the boys

**[29~30]** 다음 글을 읽고 물음에 답하시오.

My favorite sport is basketball. However, I wasn't really good at it at first. I couldn't shoot well unlike other players. Although I felt discouraged, I didn't give up. I practiced _____(A)_____ for an hour every day. This made me _____(B)_____ well. Now, I'm the best player on our team.

## 29 단어 shoot을 어법에 맞게 빈칸 (A)와 (B)에 각각 쓰시오.

(A) _____ (B) _____

## 30 다음 중 위 글의 내용과 일치하는 것은?

① The writer doesn't like basketball that much.

② The writer was very good at playing basketball from the beginning.

③ The writer shot as well as other players.

④ The writer tried hard to be good at basketball.

⑤ No other player in his team is as bad as the writer.

**[31~33]** 다음 글을 읽고 물음에 답하시오.

The boys gathered old boats and pieces of wood.

(A) Still, they didn't care. _____ⓐ_____, they built excellent skills and enjoyed playing soccer more.

(B) It was shaky and had nails everywhere. The ball and the boys would often fall into the sea, so the field was always wet and slippery. They had no shoes so they had to play in bare feet.

(C) They put the boats together and nailed the wood to them. After much hard work, they finally had a floating field.

## 31 다음 빈칸 ⓐ에 들어갈 말로 적절한 것을 모두 고르시오.

① On the other hand ② Actually

③ In fact ④ Probably

⑤ Unfortunately

## 32 자연스러운 글이 되도록 (A)~(C)를 바르게 배열한 것은?

① (A) – (C) – (B) ② (B) – (A) – (C)

③ (B) – (C) – (A) ④ (C) – (A) – (B)

⑤ (C) – (B) – (A)

## 33 Write the reason why the boys had to play soccer in bare feet. Use the phrase 'It's because.'

➡ _____

[01~02] 다음 대화를 읽고 물음에 답하시오.

Mina: Tim, have you heard of the Gobi Desert?
Tim: Yes, I have. Isn't it in Mongolia and China?
Mina: Yes, it is. Yesterday, I saw a TV show about people who crossed the desert on foot.
Tim: Only on foot?
Mina: Yes, it took them about 51 days.
Tim: Wow, that's amazing. I want to experience life in the desert but I don't want to cross it on foot.
Mina: Well, I want to try and cross the Gobi Desert in 50 days.

출제율 90%

**01** 위 대화의 내용과 일치하도록 빈칸을 완성하시오.

Mina saw a TV show about people crossing the Gobi desert on (A)_____. It took them about (B)_____ days. She felt interesting and told it to Tim. When she explained about it, Tim also surprised and said that he wanted (C)_____ _____ _____ _____ _____. However, Tim didn't want to (D)_____ _____ _____ _____ _____. On the other hand, Mina, who had a brave heart, wanted to (E)_____ _____ _____ _____ _____ _____.

출제율 100%

**02** 위 대화에서 나타난 Mina의 성격으로 적절한 것은?

① brave          ② polite
③ shy            ④ thoughtful
⑤ honest

[03~05] 다음 대화를 읽고 물음에 답하시오.

Father: Emily, are you excited about your match on Saturday?
Emily: Not really. We're playing against a strong team. I think we'll lose.
Father: (A) Don't say that. Have you heard about the Greek team in the 2004 Euro Cup?
Emily: (B) What about them?
Father: (C) They were a weak team, so everyone thought that they would lose.
Emily: (D) What happened?
Father: (E) They played as a team and worked hard. Finally, they won the Euro Cup. So, don't give up.
Emily: Thanks, Dad. We'll try our best.

출제율 100%

**03** 위 대화의 (A)~(E) 중 주어진 문장이 들어가기에 적절한 곳은?

No, I haven't.

① (A)    ② (B)    ③ (C)    ④ (D)    ⑤ (E)

출제율 90%

**04** 위 대화에서 다음의 영영풀이가 가리키는 것을 찾아 쓰시오.

a contest between two or more players or teams

➡ _____

출제율 95%

**05** 위 대화를 읽고 대답할 수 <u>없는</u> 것은?

① What is Emily going to do on Saturday?
② Which team won the 2004 Euro Cup?
③ How could the Greek team win the 2004 Euro Cup?
④ Has Emily heard about the Greek team in the 2004 Euro Cup?
⑤ What did Emily do to win the game?

[06~08] 다음 대화를 읽고 물음에 답하시오.

Mina: Tim, have you heard of the Gobi Desert?

Tim: _____(A)_____ Isn't ⓐit in Mongolia and China?

Mina: Yes, ⓑit is. Yesterday, I saw a TV show about people who crossed the desert on foot.

Tim: Only on foot?

Mina: Yes, ⓒit took them about 51 days.

Tim: Wow, that's amazing. I want to experience life in the desert but I don't want to cross ⓓit on foot.

Mina: Well, I want to try and cross ⓔit in 50 days.

**출제율 90%**

**06** 위 대화의 빈칸 (A)에 들어갈 말로 적절한 것은?

① Yes, I do.
② Yes, I have.
③ Yes, I did.
④ No, I didn't.
⑤ No, I don't.

**출제율 100%**

**07** 위 대화의 밑줄 친 ⓐ~ⓔ 중 가리키는 대상이 나머지와 다른 것은?

① ⓐ
② ⓑ
③ ⓒ
④ ⓓ
⑤ ⓔ

**출제율 95%**

**08** 위 대화를 읽고 대답할 수 없는 것은?

① When did Mina see a TV show about people crossing the Gobi Desert?
② How long did it take people to cross the Gobi Desert on foot on a TV show?
③ Where is the Gobi Desert located?
④ What does Mina want to do in the Gobi Desert?
⑤ Why doesn't Tim want to cross the Goby Desert on foot?

[09~10] 다음 대화를 읽고 물음에 답하시오.

Suji: Hojun, are you going to try out for the school ice hockey team? The new season is about to start.

Hojun: I'm not sure.

Suji: Why not?

Hojun: I heard that Tony and Brad are also trying out for the team. They're so good.

Suji: Well, you're also good at ice hockey, so don't give up!

Hojun: Okay, I'll try my best. Thanks a lot.

**출제율 95%**

**09** Which team did Tony and Brad try out for?

➡ _____

**출제율 90%**

**10** What did Hojun promise to do?

➡ _____

**출제율 100%**

**11** 다음 빈칸에 들어갈 말이 바르게 짝지어진 것은?

_____ Mina needed a passport photo, she had her picture _____ by her little brother who didn't know how to take pictures well.

① Because – taking
② Although – take
③ Since – take
④ Although – took
⑤ Even though – taken

**출제율 95%**

**12** 다음 중 어법상 바르지 않은 것은?

Yesterday, I ①asked my roommate ② to let ③me ④to use her shoe polish and she allowed me ⑤to use it.

① ② ③ ④ ⑤

**13** 알맞은 부사절 접속사로 시작하여 다음 두 문장을 하나의 문장으로 쓰시오. *출제율 95%*

> The weather was very cold. She went out for a walk.

➡ _____

_____

**14** 다음 빈칸에 적절하지 <u>않은</u> 것은? *출제율 90%*

> Mrs. Wilson _____ the children wash their hands before dinner.

① helps  ② makes  ③ lets
④ has  ⑤ gets

**15** 다음 중 우리말을 영어로 바르게 옮긴 것은? (2개) *출제율 95%*

① 비록 그는 몸이 아팠지만, 수업에 출석했다.
　→ He attended class although he was sick.
② 알람이 울렸지만, 나는 일어나지 않았다.
　→ Despite the alarm rang, I didn't get up.
③ 비록 그가 영국에서 태어났을지라도, 그는 한국 소년이다.
　→ He is a Korean boy because he was born in England.
④ Jane은 웨이터에게 그녀의 차를 가지고 오라고 하였다.
　→ Jane had the waiter brought her tea.
⑤ 그 경찰관은 그가 차에서 내리게 했다.
　→ The police officer had him get out of his car.

**16** 단어 take를 어법에 맞게 빈칸에 쓰시오. *출제율 85%*

> We had a professional photographer _____ pictures of everyone at the wedding. We had over 50 pictures _____.

**[17~18]** 다음 글을 읽고 물음에 답하시오.

> One day, a boy brought a poster about a soccer tournament.
>
> (A) Some even came to watch the game. This made the boys feel better. At first, people saw them as the weakest team.
>
> (B) They decided to give it a try. When they were about to leave, the villagers gave them new shoes and uniforms.
>
> (C) However, when the tournament started, the soccer team surprised everyone.

**17** 자연스러운 글이 되도록 (A)~(C)를 바르게 배열하시오. *출제율 100%*

➡ _____

**18** 위 글의 내용에 맞게 빈칸에 알맞은 말을 쓰시오. *출제율 85%*

> _____ people thought the team was the weakest team, they were _____ by the team when the tournament started.

**[19~21]** 다음 글을 읽고 물음에 답하시오.

On the day of the semi-final, it was raining hard. They were losing ___(A)___ two goals and it looked impossible to win.

"The other team is so strong," they thought.

But the boys didn't give up. They took off their shoes during the second half and the game changed completely. They played better in the rain thanks to the slippery field at home. Although they lost by a score of three to two, still, they felt proud of themselves. They didn't give up when they were losing. They tried their best until the end.

출제율 90%

**19** 다음 중 빈칸 (A)에 들어갈 말로 가장 적절한 것은?

① in   ② on   ③ to   ④ by   ⑤ at

출제율 95%

**20** 다음 중 위 글의 내용과 일치하는 것은?

① 결승전 날에 비가 심하게 내렸다.
② 소년들의 팀은 처음에 두 골 차이로 이기고 있었다.
③ 소년들은 전반전에 신발을 벗었다.
④ 소년들은 빗속에서 경기를 더 잘하였다.
⑤ 소년들은 3대 2로 경기를 이겼다.

출제율 90%

**21** How did the boys feel about themselves after the game? Answer in English with a full sentence.

➡ _____

**[22~24]** 다음 글을 읽고 물음에 답하시오.

**Dear Koh Panyee Soccer Team**

Hello, I became your fan after ①watching one of your matches. Everyone thought you would lose because the other team ②was strong. But you didn't give up. During the second half, I was surprised ③to see you play in bare feet. You were playing better than before! I guess ④playing soccer on a field in the sea helped you a lot. ⑤Despite you lost by a score of three to two, I became a fan of your team. Hope to see you soon.

Yours,
Fern Yahtie

출제율 90%

**22** 위 글의 ①~⑤ 중 어법상 바르지 않은 것은?

①   ②   ③   ④   ⑤

출제율 85%

**23** 위 글의 내용에 맞게 빈칸에 알맞은 말을 쓰시오.

Fern thought playing in bare feet made the players _____ _____ _____
_____ .

출제율 100%

**24** 다음 중 위 글의 내용과 일치하는 것은?

① Fern Yahtie is not interested in soccer at all.
② Koh Panyee Soccer Team looked as strong as all the other teams.
③ Koh Panyee Soccer Team members played the game without any shoes on during the second half.
④ Koh Panyee Soccer Team won the game in the end.
⑤ Koh Panyee Soccer Team lost the game because they played in bare feet.

[01~03] 다음 대화를 읽고 물음에 답하시오.

> Mina: Tim, (A)고비 사막에 대해 들어 보았니? (of, Gobi Desert)
>
> Tim: Yes, I have. Isn't it in Mongolia and China?
>
> Mina: Yes, it is. Yesterday, I saw a TV show about people who crossed the desert on foot.
>
> Tim: Only on foot?
>
> Mina: Yes, it took them about 51 days.
>
> Tim: Wow, that's amazing. I want to experience life in the desert but I don't want to cross it on foot.
>
> Mina: Well, I want to try and cross the Gobi Desert in 50 days.

**01** 위 대화의 밑줄 친 (A)의 우리말을 주어진 단어를 사용하여 영작하시오.

➡ _____

중요

**02** How long did it take people to cross the Gobi Desert on foot on a TV show?

➡ _____

**03** What does Mina want to try?

➡ _____
_____

중요

**04** 적절한 부사절 접속사로 시작하여 다음 두 문장을 하나의 문장으로 표현하시오.

> He doesn't have time. He tries to exercise every day.

➡ _____
_____

중요

**05** 주어진 단어를 바르게 배열하여 다음 일기를 완성하시오. 필요할 경우 어형을 바꾸시오.

> Today we had my mother's birthday party. My dad baked a cake. He (write / have / me) letters on the cake with chocolate cream. Then, we made some cookies. Lastly, he (me / clean / make) the table.

➡ _____

**06** 주어진 어구를 활용하여 다음 우리말을 영어로 쓰시오. (접속사로 시작할 것)

> 비록 나는 매우 피곤했지만, 늦게까지 깨어 있었다. (stay up late)

➡ _____

**07** 주어진 단어를 어법에 맞게 빈칸에 쓰시오.

> When Scott went shopping, he found a jacket that he really liked. After he had the sleeves _____(shorten), it fit him perfectly.

**08** 다음 우리말에 맞게 빈칸에 알맞은 말을 네 단어로 쓰시오.

> 그의 얼굴에 나타난 슬픈 표정은 내게 그를 향해 미안함을 느끼게 했다.
> ➡ The sad expression on his face _____ _____ _____ _____ for him.

_____(A)_____
Who? Boys in Koh Panyee
What?
The boys make a soccer team but there is no place to play soccer. __(B)__, they aren't discouraged. They make a floating field. It's shaky and they play in bare feet but they're happy. One day, (C)그들은 토너먼트에 참가한다. Will they make it to the finals?

**09** 주어진 단어를 바르게 배열하여 빈칸 (A)에 들어갈 위 글의 제목을 완성하시오.

> (courage / team / with / soccer / a)

➡ _____

**10** 다음 글을 참고하여 빈칸 (B)에 들어갈 알맞은 말을 쓰시오.

> You use this word when you are adding a comment which is surprising or which contrasts with what has just been said.

➡ _____

**11** 위 글의 내용에 맞게 빈칸에 알맞은 말을 쓰시오.

> After making their own soccer field, the boys are happy even though _____ _____ _____ _____ _____ _____ _____ _____.

**12** 주어진 단어를 활용하여 밑줄 친 우리말 (C)를 영어로 쓰시오.

> (take)

➡ _____

On the day of the semi-final, it was raining hardly. They were losing by two goals and it looked impossible to win.
"The other team is so strong," they thought.
But the boys didn't give up. They took off their shoes during the second half and the game changed completely. They played better in the rain thanks to the slippery field at home. Although they lost by a score of three to two, still, they felt proud of themselves. (A)They didn't give up when they were losing. They tried their best until the end.

**13** How many goals did the team get in the end? Answer in English with a full sentence.

➡ _____

**14** 위 글에서 문맥상 어색한 어휘 하나를 찾아 바르게 고치시오.

_____ ➡ _____

**15** 빈칸에 알맞은 말을 써서 밑줄 친 문장 (A)와 같은 의미의 문장을 완성하시오.

> They didn't give up _____ they were losing.

**16** 위 글의 내용에 맞게 빈칸에 알맞은 말을 쓰시오.

> The slippery field at home made them _____ _____ _____ _____ _____.

**01** 다음 대화의 내용과 일치하도록 호준이의 일기를 완성하시오.

> Suji: Hojun, are you going to try out for the school ice hockey team? The new season is about to start.
>
> Hojun: I'm not sure.
>
> Suji: Why not?
>
> Hojun: I heard that Tony and Brad are also trying out for the team. They're so good.
>
> Suji: Well, you're also good at ice hockey, so don't give up!
>
> Hojun: Okay, I'll try my best. Thanks a lot.

↓

> Mon, Dec 9th, 2019
> I was thinking about whether I would try out for (A)_____. Actually, I was not confident because I heard that (B)_____ tried out for the team. I knew they're so good players. When I talked with Suji, she encouraged me not to (C)_____. She said I'm also good at ice hockey. I promised her to (D)_____.

**02** 사역동사와 주어진 단어를 활용하여 여러 가지 문장을 쓰시오.

> clean   go out   do   take

(1) _____

(2) _____

(3) _____

(4) _____

# 단원별 모의고사

**01** 다음 영영풀이가 가리키는 것을 고르시오.

> a thing done successfully, typically by effort, courage, or skill

① tournament    ② project
③ courage    ④ experience
⑤ achievement

**02** 다음 우리말에 맞게 빈칸에 알맞은 말을 쓰시오.

(1) 준결승전 날, 비가 심하게 내리고 있었다.
➡ On the day of the _____, it was raining hard.

(2) 그것은 흔들리고 그들은 맨발로 뛴다.
➡ It's _____ and they play in bare feet.

(3) 나는 다른 선수들과 달리 슛을 잘할 수 없었다.
➡ I couldn't _____ well unlike other players.

**03** 다음 문장의 빈칸에 들어갈 말이 순서대로 짝지어진 것은?

> (A) I decided to _____ out for the math contest.
> (B) Even though there are many difficulties, don't _____ up.
> (C) In Korea, people usually _____ off their shoes when they enter the rooms.

① try – take – give
② try – give – take
③ give – try – take
④ give – take – try
⑤ take – give – try

**[04~05]** 다음 대화를 읽고 물음에 답하시오.

Sora: Alex, have you heard about this year's "Ugly Sweater Party?"
Alex: Of course, I have. It's on December 5th, right?
Sora: (A) That's right. Are you going to go?
Alex: (B) I want to, but I don't have an ugly sweater.
Sora: (C) You can have it if you want.
Alex: (D) Thanks. That would be great.
Sora: (E) Let's meet in front of the Student Center and go inside together.
Alex: Sure. See you then.

**04** 위 대화의 (A)~(E) 중 다음 주어진 문장이 들어가기에 적절한 곳은?

> I have one that I don't wear at home.

① (A)   ② (B)   ③ (C)   ④ (D)   ⑤ (E)

**05** 위 대화의 내용과 일치하지 <u>않는</u> 것은?

① 소라와 Alex는 올해의 "못생긴 스웨터 파티"에 대해 알고 있다.
② 올해의 "못생긴 스웨터 파티"는 12월 5일에 열린다.
③ Alex는 못생긴 스웨터가 없어서 새로 살 것이다.
④ 소라는 입지 않는 못생긴 스웨터 한 벌을 갖고 있다.
⑤ 소라와 Alex는 학생회관 앞에서 만나서 같이 들어갈 것이다.

**06** 다음 글을 읽고 대답할 수 <u>없는</u> 것은?

> W: What can you do to be healthy? First, try to exercise every day. Second, try to eat healthy food. Don't eat too much fast food. Third, wash your hands before meals. Do these tips sound hard to do? Well, take one step at a time and don't give up. Then you'll live a healthy life.

① What is the woman talking about?
② What should we eat to be healthy?
③ What should we do every day to live a healthy life?
④ What should we do before meals?
⑤ Which tip is the most important to be healthy?

**07** 다음 우리말과 일치하도록 주어진 어구를 사용하여 영작하시오.

(1) 그것은 흔들렸고 어디나 못이 있었다.
　　(had, everywhere)

　　➡ _____

(2) 소년들은 낡은 배와 나뭇조각들을 모았다.
　　(pieces, boats)

　　➡ _____

**[08~09]** 다음 대화를 읽고 물음에 답하시오.

> Suji: Hojun, are you going to try out for the school ice hockey team? The new season is about to start.
> Hojun: I'm not (A)[sure / doubtful].
> Suji: Why not?
> Hojun: I heard that _____ⓐ_____. They're

so good.
> Suji: Well, you're also good at ice hockey, so don't (B)[cheer / give] up!
> Hojun: Okay, I'll try my (C)[better / best]. Thanks a lot.

**08** 위 대화의 빈칸 ⓐ에 들어갈 말을 주어진 단어를 모두 배열하여 영작하시오.

> ┤ 보기 ├
> also / the / trying / Tony and Brad / for / team / are / out

➡ _____

**09** 위 대화의 빈칸 (A)~(C)에 들어갈 말이 바르게 짝지어진 것은?

① sure – cheer – better
② sure – give – best
③ sure – give – better
④ doubtful – give – best
⑤ doubtful – cheer – better

**[10~12]** 다음 대화를 읽고 물음에 답하시오.

> Father: Emily, are you excited about your match on Saturday?
> Emily: Not really. We're playing against a strong team. I think we'll lose.
> Father: Don't say that. Have you heard about the Greek team in the 2004 Euro Cup?
> Emily: No, I haven't. What about ⓐthem?
> Father: ⓑThey were a weak team, so ⓒeveryone thought that they would lose.
> Emily: What happened?
> Father: ⓓThey played as a team and worked hard. Finally, ⓔthey won the Euro Cup. So, don't give up.
> Emily: Thanks, Dad. We'll try our best.

**10** 위 대화의 밑줄 친 ⓐ~ⓔ 중 가리키는 대상이 나머지와 다른 것은?

① ⓐ ② ⓑ ③ ⓒ ④ ⓓ ⑤ ⓔ

**11** Although the Greek team was a weak team, how could they win the 2004 Euro Cup?

➡ _____

**12** 위 대화의 내용과 일치하도록 빈칸을 완성하시오.

> Emily's father told Emily how (A)_____ _____ _____ won the 2004 Euro Cup because her father didn't want her to (B)_____ _____ her match on (C)_____. After talking with her father, Emily decided to (D)_____ _____ _____.

**13** 주어진 문장과 같은 의미의 문장을 쓰시오.

> I had Tom repair my shoes.
> = I had my shoes _____ _____ _____.

**14** 다음 중 어법상 바른 문장은?

① Peeling onions always makes me crying.
② Despite she felt scared, she had to stay cool.
③ The man had the restaurant ran by his wife.
④ Although you didn't invite me to the party I didn't care.
⑤ I had my computer fixed by Ann.

**15** 다음 빈칸에 들어갈 말이 바르게 짝지어진 것은?

> Candace had her children _____ them _____ out their garage.

① to help – to clean ② helped – cleaned
③ help – to clean ④ help – to cleaning
⑤ helping – cleaning

**[16~18]** 다음 글을 읽고 물음에 답하시오.

> The boys ①gathered old boats and pieces of wood. They put the boats together and ②nailed the wood to them. After much hard work, they finally had a ③floating field. It was shaky and had nails everywhere. The ball and the boys would often fall into the sea, so the field was always ④dry and slippery. They had no shoes so they had to play in bare feet. Still, they ⑤didn't care. In fact, they built excellent skills and enjoyed playing soccer more.

**16** 위 글의 ①~⑤ 중 글의 흐름상 어색한 것은?

① ② ③ ④ ⑤

**17** 다음 중 위 글의 내용과 일치하는 것은?

① The boys put apart the boats.
② The boys wanted someone to make their soccer field.
③ There were no nails on the field.
④ The boys hammered the nails by themselves.
⑤ The boys fenced the field in order not to fall into the sea.

**18** 다음과 같이 풀이되는 말을 위 글에서 찾아 쓰시오.

> not covered by clothing, shoes, a hat, etc.

➡ _____

**20** 다음 중 밑줄 친 (A)와 쓰임이 같은 것은?

① It enables us to live our lives comfortably.
② It is not a great idea to tell him the truth.
③ Is there any chance to see him again?
④ They tried hard to make the machine work.
⑤ We hope to see you soon.

**[21~23]** 다음 글을 읽고 물음에 답하시오.

One day, a boy brought a poster about a soccer tournament. ①They decided to give it a try. When ②they were about to leave, the villagers gave ③them new shoes and uniforms. Some of ④them even came to watch the game. This made the boys feel better. At first, people saw ⑤them as the weakest team. However, when the tournament started, the soccer team surprised everyone.

On the day of the semi-final, it was raining hard. They were losing by two goals and it looked impossible to win.

"The other team is so strong," they thought.

But the boys didn't give up.

**[19~20]** 다음 글을 읽고 물음에 답하시오.

Koh Panyee was a small floating village in the middle of the sea. Although the boys in the village never played soccer before, they loved watching it on TV. One day, the boys decided to make their own soccer team. However, people laughed at their idea.

"That's impossible."

"What makes you say so?"

"Look around. Where are you going to play soccer?"

The villagers were right. The boys had no place (A)to play soccer. They were discouraged.

"Don't give up! We can still play soccer."

"How?"

"Let's make our own soccer field."

**21** 위 글의 ①~⑤ 중 지칭하는 것이 <u>다른</u> 하나는?

①          ②          ③          ④          ⑤

**22** What did the boys decided to do after seeing a poster? Answer in English with a full sentence.

➡ _____

**19** 위 글의 내용과 일치하지 <u>않는</u> 것은?

① Koh Panyee was floating on the sea.
② The boys in the village made up their mind to make their own soccer team.
③ What people said about the boys' idea had a point because there was no place to play soccer.
④ The boys decided to make their own soccer field so that they could play soccer.
⑤ People in the village encouraged the boys to make their soccer team.

**23** 다음은 경기에 참가한 소년의 말이다. 위 글의 표현을 활용하여 영어로 쓰시오.

> 비록 이기는 것이 불가능해 보였지만, 우리는 포기하지 않았습니다.

➡ _____

_____

# INSIGHT
## on the textbook
교과서 파헤치기

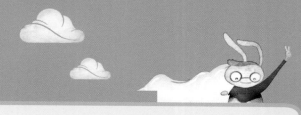

※ 다음 영어를 우리말로 쓰시오.

| 01 | flavor |
| 02 | safe |
| 03 | difference |
| 04 | escape |
| 05 | fill |
| 06 | freezer |
| 07 | instead |
| 08 | sink |
| 09 | float |
| 10 | lightning |
| 11 | pressure |
| 12 | secret |
| 13 | behind |
| 14 | prepare |
| 15 | sunburn |
| 16 | expand |
| 17 | trick |
| 18 | material |
| 19 | compare |
| 20 | absorb |
| 21 | flame |

| 22 | contract |
| 23 | disappear |
| 24 | experiment |
| 25 | dry |
| 26 | confuse |
| 27 | rise |
| 28 | weigh |
| 29 | magic |
| 30 | sunscreen |
| 31 | hold |
| 32 | candle |
| 33 | practice |
| 34 | necessary |
| 35 | for a long time |
| 36 | cool down |
| 37 | sign up for |
| 38 | give it a try |
| 39 | stick to |
| 40 | burn out |
| 41 | pick out |
| 42 | see through |
| 43 | turn A into B |

※ 다음 우리말을 영어로 쓰시오.

01 동전

02 채우다

03 연습

04 마술, 마법

05 사라지다

06 마른, 비가 오지 않는

07 팽창하다

08 양초

09 볕에 탐

10 맛

11 가라앉다

12 흡수하다

13 비밀

14 대신에

15 번개

16 재료, 물질

17 자외선 차단제

18 차이, 차이점

19 수축하다

20 섞다

21 실험

22 필요한

23 안전한

24 마술, 속임수

25 불꽃

26 준비하다

27 혼동하게 하다

28 뜨다

29 탈출하다, (액체, 가스가) 새다

30 비교하다

31 압력

32 무게를 재다

33 오르다, 올라가다

34 냉동고

35 골라내다

36 타 버리다

37 ~을 (바꾸지 않고) 고수하다

38 오랫동안

39 차가워지다

40 A가 B로 변하다

41 ~을 신청하다

42 시도해 보다

43 속을 들여다 보다

※ 다음 영영풀이에 알맞은 단어를 <보기>에서 골라 쓴 후, 우리말 뜻을 쓰시오.

1  _____ : to become impossible to see: _____

2  _____ : to become smaller: _____

3  _____ : to combine two or more substances so that they become a single
      substance: _____

4  _____ : to go down below the surface of water: _____

5  _____ : to increase in size, range, or amount: _____

6  _____ : to rest on top of a liquid or in the air: _____

7  _____ : to mistake one person or thing for another: _____

8  _____ : a substance that things can be made from: _____

9  _____ : something done to surprise or confuse someone: _____

10 _____ : a device or room for freezing food or keeping it frozen: _____

11 _____ : to find how heavy someone or something is: _____

12 _____ : to take in something in a natural or gradual way: _____

13 _____ : having the power to make impossible things happen: _____

14 _____ : a scientific test that is done in order to study what happens and to gain
      new knowledge: _____

15 _____ : a piece of information that is kept hidden from other people: _____

16 _____ : the activity of doing something again and again in order to become
      better at it: _____

| 보기 | | | |
|---|---|---|---|
| secret | expand | contract | absorb |
| trick | magic | weigh | confuse |
| practice | float | sink | experiment |
| freezer | disappear | material | mix |

※ 다음 우리말과 일치하도록 빈칸에 알맞은 말을 쓰시오.

### Listen & Speak 1 A

W: Today we'll make ice cream. _____ _____ do you want to make? _____ _____ strawberry? _____, mix two cups of milk, two cups of heavy cream, and _____ _____ _____ of sugar. _____, _____ five strawberries _____ small pieces. Then, _____ everything together and put it in the _____. That's it. It's _____ _____ _____, _____ it? _____ _____ you _____ _____ it at home?

W: 오늘 우리는 아이스크림을 만들 거예요. 여러분은 어느 맛을 만들고 싶은가요? 딸기는 어때요? 첫째로, 우유 2컵, 헤비 크림 2컵, 설탕 1/2컵을 섞으세요. 다음, 딸기 5개를 작은 조각으로 자르세요. 그 다음에, 모든 것을 섞어서 냉동실에 넣으세요. 이게 다예요. 만들기 쉽죠, 그렇지 않나요? 집에서 아이스크림을 만들어 보는 게 어때요?

### Listen & Speak 1 B

B: Yujin, _____ did you _____ the eggs in water?

G: I'm _____ _____ the bad eggs.

B: _____ _____ are fresh, and _____ ones are not?

G: Eggs _____ _____ _____ _____ are fresh. When eggs _____ in water, they're not fresh. You _____ _____ them.

B: That's _____. Why do the bad eggs _____?

G: _____ they have gas _____. The gas _____ _____ the air in a _____.

B: Oh, I see.

B: 유진아, 왜 달걀을 물속에 넣었니?

G: 나는 상한 달걀을 골라내는 중이야.

B: 어느 달걀이 신선하고 어느 것이 신선하지 않은 거야?

G: 물에 가라앉는 달걀은 신선해. 달걀이 물에 뜨면, 그건 신선하지 않아. 그것들을 먹으면 안 돼.

B: 그거 재미있다. 상한 달걀은 왜 물에 뜨는 거니?

G: 상한 달걀은 속에 가스가 차기 때문이야. 가스가 풍선 속의 공기 같은 역할을 하거든.

B: 아, 이제 이해했다.

### Listen & Speak 2 A

B: Ms. Jeong, does _____ _____ _____ water _____ more when there's a fish in it?

W: Yes, it does. We _____ _____ _____ it now.

B: But how? We don't have a _____.

W: We _____ _____ a finger _____ _____ a fish.

B: _____ will that _____?

W: I'll _____ a glass of water first. Then I will _____ my finger in the water and _____ it to _____.

B: Oh, I _____ _____ _____ see the _____.

B: 정 선생님, 물속에 물고기가 있을 때 물 1잔의 무게가 더 무겁나요?

W: 응, 그렇단다. 우리는 지금 실험해 볼 수 있어.

B: 하지만 어떻게요? 물고기가 없는데요.

W: 우리는 물고기 대신 손가락을 사용할 수 있단다.

B: 어떻게 할 수 있어요?

W: 먼저 물 1잔의 무게를 잴 거야. 그 다음에 비교하기 위해 물속에 손가락을 넣고 무게를 잴 거란다.

B: 아, 차이를 빨리 알고 싶어요.

### Listen & Speak 2 B

**King Sejong:** It _____ _____ _____ a long time.

**Jang Yeongsil:** Yes. The _____ _____ is _____ too long. The farmers are very _____.

**King Sejong:** We _____ do something _____ _____ them.

**Jang Yeongsil:** How about making a _____ _____?

**King Sejong:** A clock? _____ will that _____?

**Jang Yeongsil:** The clock will show the time and the _____. We can use it _____ _____ _____ the _____ _____.

**King Sejong:** That _____ _____ a good idea. But who's _____ _____ make it?

**Jang Yeongsil:** I'll _____ _____ _____ _____. I know _____ _____ about time and the seasons.

**King Sejong:** Okay, I _____ _____ _____ _____ _____.

### Real Life Communication A

**Brian:** Mina, will you _____ our tennis club?

**Mina:** It _____ _____, but I _____ _____ _____ a special class this _____.

**Brian:** _____ _____ did you sign up for?

**Mina:** I signed up for a _____ _____. I _____ _____ _____ learn new magic _____ there.

**Brian:** That sounds _____! _____ _____ _____ magic tricks before?

**Mina:** Yes, I learned some before, but I need _____ _____.

**Brian:** I hope I can see your magic tricks _____ _____.

### Let's Check

**B:** What _____ you _____, Jiwon?

**G:** I'm reading a book about _____ and _____.

**B:** That _____ _____.

**G:** Yes. This book _____ 100 magic tricks that _____. I've _____ _____ _____ of them.

**B:** That's _____. Can you show me _____ of the tricks?

**G:** Sure. I can show you a _____ _____ now.

**B:** Great! I _____ _____ _____ _____ it.

---

King Sejong: 오랫동안 비가 오지 않는구나.

Jang Yeongsil: 그렇습니다. 건기가 너무 오래 계속되고 있습니다. 농부들이 아주 걱정하고 있습니다.

King Sejong: 그들을 돕기 위해 뭐든 해야 한다.

Jang Yeongsil: 특별한 시계를 만드는 것은 어떨까요?

King Sejong: 시계? 그것이 어떻게 도움이 되겠느냐?

Jang Yeongsil: 시계는 시간과 계절을 알려줄 겁니다. 건기를 준비하기 위해 시계를 사용할 수 있습니다.

King Sejong: 그거 좋은 생각 같구나. 하지만 누가 시계를 만들겠느냐?

Jang Yeongsil: 제가 한번 해 보겠습니다. 저는 시간과 계절에 대해 많이 알고 있습니다.

King Sejong: 좋다. 네 시계를 빨리 보고 싶구나.

---

Brian: 미나야, 우리 테니스 동아리에 가입할래?

Mina: 재미있겠다. 하지만 나는 이번 가을에 특별 수업에 등록했어.

Brian: 무슨 수업에 등록했니?

Mina: 마술 수업에 등록했어. 거기서 새로운 마술 묘기를 빨리 배우고 싶어.

Brian: 그거 재미있겠다! 전에 마술 묘기를 배운 적이 있니?

Mina: 응, 전에 몇 가지 배웠어, 하지만 더 연습을 해야 해.

Brian: 언젠가 네 마술 묘기를 볼 수 있길 바라.

---

B: 지원아, 뭘 읽고 있니?

G: 마술과 과학에 관한 책을 읽고 있어.

B: 그거 재미있겠다.

G: 응. 이 책은 과학을 사용하는 100가지 마술을 소개하고 있어. 나는 그 중에 절반 정도를 익혔어.

B: 멋지다. 마술 중 몇 가지를 보여줄 수 있니?

G: 물론이지. 지금 풍선 마술을 보여줄 수 있어.

B: 멋지다! 빨리 보고 싶어.

※ 다음 우리말에 맞도록 대화를 영어로 쓰시오.

### Listen & Speak 1 A

W: _____

_____

_____

_____

W: 오늘 우리는 아이스크림을 만들 거예요. 여러분은 어느 맛을 만들고 싶은가요? 딸기는 어때요? 첫째로, 우유 2컵, 헤비 크림 2컵, 설탕 1/2컵을 섞으세요. 다음, 딸기 5개를 작은 조각으로 자르세요. 그 다음에, 모든 것을 섞어서 냉동실에 넣으세요. 이게 다예요. 만들기 쉽죠, 그렇지 않나요? 집에서 아이스크림을 만들어 보는 게 어때요?

### Listen & Speak 1 B

B: _____

G: _____

B: _____

G: _____

B: _____

G: _____

B: _____

B: 유진아, 왜 달걀을 물속에 넣었니?
G: 나는 상한 달걀을 골라내는 중이야.
B: 어느 달걀이 신선하고 어느 것이 신선하지 않은 거야?
G: 물에 가라앉는 달걀은 신선해. 달걀이 물에 뜨면, 그건 신선하지 않아. 그것들을 먹으면 안 돼.
B: 그거 재미있다. 상한 달걀은 왜 물에 뜨는 거니?
G: 상한 달걀은 속에 가스가 차기 때문이야. 가스가 풍선 속의 공기 같은 역할을 하거든.
B: 아, 이제 이해했다.

### Listen & Speak 2 A

B: _____

W: _____

B: _____

W: _____

B: _____

W: _____

B: _____

B: 정 선생님, 물속에 물고기가 있을 때 물 1잔의 무게가 더 무겁나요?
W: 응, 그렇단다. 우리는 지금 실험해 볼 수 있어.
B: 하지만 어떻게요? 물고기가 없는데요.
W: 우리는 물고기 대신 손가락을 사용할 수 있단다.
B: 어떻게 할 수 있어요?
W: 먼저 물 1잔의 무게를 잴 거야. 그 다음에 비교하기 위해 물속에 손가락을 넣고 무게를 잴 거란다.
B: 아, 차이를 빨리 알고 싶어요.

## Listen & Speak 2 B

King Sejong: _____

Jang Yeongsil: _____

King Sejong: _____

Jang Yeongsil: _____

King Sejong: _____

Jang Yeongsil: _____

_____

King Sejong: _____

Jang Yeongsil: _____

King Sejong: _____

King Sejong: 오랫동안 비가 오지 않는구나.

Jang Yeongsil: 그렇습니다. 건기가 너무 오래 계속되고 있습니다. 농부들이 아주 걱정하고 있습니다.

King Sejong: 그들을 돕기 위해 뭐든 해야 한다.

Jang Yeongsil: 특별한 시계를 만드는 것은 어떨까요?

King Sejong: 시계? 그것이 어떻게 도움이 되겠느냐?

Jang Yeongsil: 시계는 시간과 계절을 알려줄 겁니다. 건기를 준비하기 위해 시계를 사용할 수 있습니다.

King Sejong: 그거 좋은 생각 같구나. 하지만 누가 시계를 만들겠느냐?

Jang Yeongsil: 제가 한번 해 보겠습니다. 저는 시간과 계절에 대해 많이 알고 있습니다.

King Sejong: 좋다, 네 시계를 빨리 보고 싶구나.

## Real Life Communication A

Brian: _____

Mina: _____

Brian: _____

Mina: _____

Brian: _____

Mina: _____

Brian: _____

Brian: 미나야, 우리 테니스 동아리에 가입할래?

Mina: 재미있겠다. 하지만 나는 이번 가을에 특별 수업에 등록했어.

Brian: 무슨 수업에 등록했니?

Mina: 마술 수업에 등록했어. 거기서 새로운 마술 묘기를 빨리 배우고 싶어.

Brian: 그거 재미있겠다! 전에 마술 묘기를 배운 적이 있니?

Mina: 응, 전에 몇 가지 배웠어, 하지만 더 연습을 해야 해.

Brian: 언젠가 네 마술 묘기를 볼 수 있길 바라.

## Let's Check

B: _____

G: _____

B: _____

G: _____

_____

B: _____

G: _____

B: _____

B: 지원아, 뭘 읽고 있니?

G: 마술과 과학에 관한 책을 읽고 있어.

B: 그거 재미있겠다.

G: 응. 이 책은 과학을 사용하는 100가지 마술을 소개하고 있어. 나는 그 중에 절반 정도를 익혔어.

B: 멋지다. 마술 중 몇 가지를 보여줄 수 있니?

G: 물론이지. 지금 풍선 마술을 보여줄 수 있어.

B: 멋지다! 빨리 보고 싶어.

※ 다음 우리말과 일치하도록 빈칸에 알맞은 것을 골라 쓰시오.

**1** Jina: _____ _____ the _____ Science _____ Show!
A. Magic     B. to     C. welcome     D. Super

**2** _____ always _____ to _____ magic _____ .
A. exciting     B. tricks     C. see     D. it's

**3** And it's _____ exciting to _____ _____ the secrets _____ them.
A. find     B. behind     C. out     D. more

**4** Some people think the _____ of _____ is _____ .
A. magic     B. science     C. secret

**5** Today, Ken, a _____ of the School Magic Club, will use _____ to _____ his _____ .
A. perform     B. member     C. tricks     D. science

**6** Which tricks will he _____ us? I _____ _____ to see them.
A. wait     B. show     C. can't

**7** Ken: Hello, everyone. Today, I'm going to _____ you _____ _____ .
A. something     B. show     C. amazing

**8** Here's a _____ _____ _____ in it.
A. with     B. dish     C. water

**9** Now, I'll _____ a candle in the _____ of the _____ .
A. middle     B. put     C. dish

**10** Next, I'll _____ the candle and _____ it _____ a glass. "Abracadabra!"
A. cover     B. light     C. with

**11** Jina: Look at the water! _____ _____ it _____ the glass?
A. come     B. into     C. how     D. rose

**12** Ken: Air _____ when it gets _____ and creates _____ .
A. hot     B. pressure     C. expands     D. higher

**13** When it _____ cold, air _____ and creates _____ .
A. contracts     B. pressure     C. gets     D. lower

**14** When the flame _____ _____ , the air inside the glass _____ _____ .
A. pressure     B. out     C. lower     D. burnt

**15** As the air _____ down, the air _____ _____ .
A. pressure     B. cooled     C. dropped

**1** 지나: 특별 과학 마술 쇼에 오신 것을 환영합니다!

**2** 마술을 보는 것은 항상 신나는 일입니다.

**3** 그리고 마술 뒤에 숨겨진 비밀을 알아내는 것은 더 신나는 일입니다.

**4** 어떤 사람들은 마술의 비밀이 과학이라고 생각합니다.

**5** 오늘 학교 마술 동아리 회원인 Ken은 마술을 수행하기 위해 과학을 사용할 것입니다.

**6** 그는 우리에게 어떤 마술을 보여 줄까요? 무척 기다려지는군요.

**7** Ken: 안녕하세요, 여러분. 오늘, 저는 여러분에게 놀라운 무언가를 보여 주려고 합니다.

**8** 여기에 물이 담긴 접시가 있습니다.

**9** 이제, 저는 접시 한가운데에 초를 놓을 것입니다.

**10** 그다음에 초를 켜고 유리컵으로 초를 덮어 보겠습니다. "아브라카다브라!"

**11** 지나: 물을 보세요! 어째서 물이 유리컵 속으로 올라간 거지요?

**12** Ken: 공기가 뜨거워지면 팽창해서, 더 높은 압력을 만듭니다.

**13** 공기가 차가워지면 수축해서, 더 낮은 압력을 만듭니다.

**14** 불꽃이 다 타 버렸을 때, 유리컵 속의 공기는 식어 버렸습니다.

**15** 공기가 식었으므로, 기압이 낮아졌습니다.

**16** So the air _____ the glass was at a _____ _____.

A. higher        B. outside        C. pressure

**17** It _____ the _____ into the _____.

A. water        B. pushed        C. glass

**18** Ken: Now, I'm going to _____ _____ of these cups _____ _____.

A. fill        B. water        C. with        D. one

**19** I will _____ them _____ to _____ you.

A. around        B. move        C. confuse

**20** Jina, _____ _____ has the _____ in it?

A. cup        B. which        C. water

**21** Jina: That's _____! It's the _____ _____.

A. one        B. easy        C. middle

**22** Ken: Okay, _____ _____. See? No water.

A. check        B. let's

**23** Jina: Show _____ _____ _____ _____.

A. other        B. me        C. cups        D. the

**24** Ken: See? _____ _____ _____.

A. no        B. there's        C. water

**25** Jina: Wow! _____ _____ the water _____?

A. come        B. how        C. disappeared

**26** Ken: _____ the trick, I _____ a special material _____ one of the _____.

A. put        B. into        C. before        D. cups

**27** The material _____ the water and _____ it _____ jelly.

A. turned        B. absorbed        C. into

**28** Then the jelly _____ _____ the _____.

A. bottom        B. to        C. stuck

**29** If you want to _____ this trick, it's _____ to _____ cups that you can't see _____.

A. necessary        B. try        C. through        D. use

**30** Jina: Thank you _____ your great _____. It was really _____!

A. performance        B. for        C. amazing

---

**16** 그래서 유리컵 밖의 공기 압력이 더 높아졌습니다.

**17** 높아진 압력의 공기가 물을 밀어서 유리컵으로 들어가게 된 것입니다.

**18** Ken: 이제, 이 컵들 중 하나를 물로 채워 보겠습니다.

**19** 여러분을 헷갈리게 하려고 이 컵들을 섞어 보겠습니다.

**20** 지나, 어떤 컵에 물이 있을까요?

**21** 지나: 쉽네요! 가운데 컵이에요.

**22** Ken: 좋습니다. 확인해 봅시다. 보셨죠? 물이 없군요.

**23** 지나: 다른 컵들도 보여 주세요.

**24** Ken: 보셨죠? 물이 없네요.

**25** 지나: 왜 어째서 물이 사라진 거죠?

**26** Ken: 마술 전에, 저는 특별한 물질을 컵 하나에 넣어 두었습니다.

**27** 그 물질은 물을 흡수하고, 그것을 젤리로 변하게 했습니다.

**28** 그러고 나서 젤리는 컵 바닥에 달라붙었습니다.

**29** 여러분이 이 마술을 해 보고자 한다면, 속을 들여다볼 수 없는 컵을 사용해야 합니다.

**30** 지나: 멋진 공연 고맙습니다. 정말 놀라웠어요!

※ 다음 우리말과 일치하도록 빈칸에 알맞은 말을 쓰시오.

**1** Jina: _____ _____ the Super _____ _____ Show!

**2** _____ always _____ _____ _____ magic tricks.

**3** And it's more exciting _____ _____ _____ the secrets _____ them.

**4** Some people think the _____ of magic _____ _____ .

**5** Today, Ken, a member of the School Magic Club, _____ _____ _____ _____ _____ his _____ .

**6** Which tricks _____ he _____ _____ ? I can't _____ _____ _____ _____ .

**7** Ken: Hello, everyone. Today, I'm going _____ _____ _____ _____ _____ .

**8** Here's a dish _____ _____ _____ _____ .

**9** Now, I'll _____ _____ _____ in the _____ of the dish.

**10** Next, I'll _____ the candle and _____ _____ _____ a glass. "Abracadabra!"

**11** Jina: _____ _____ the water! _____ _____ it _____ _____ the glass?

**12** Ken: Air _____ when it _____ _____ and _____ _____ .

**13** When it _____ _____ , air _____ and _____ _____ .

**14** When the flame _____ _____ , the air inside the glass _____ _____ .

**15** As the air _____ _____ , the air pressure _____ .

---

**1** 지나: 특별 과학 마술 쇼에 오신 것을 환영합니다!

**2** 마술을 보는 것은 항상 신나는 일입니다.

**3** 그리고 마술 뒤에 숨겨진 비밀을 알아내는 것은 더 신나는 일입니다.

**4** 어떤 사람들은 마술의 비밀이 과학이라고 생각합니다.

**5** 오늘 학교 마술 동아리 회원인 Ken은 마술을 수행하기 위해 과학을 사용할 것입니다.

**6** 그는 우리에게 어떤 마술을 보여 줄까요? 무척 기다려지는군요.

**7** Ken: 안녕하세요, 여러분. 오늘, 저는 여러분에게 놀라운 무언가를 보여 주려고 합니다.

**8** 여기에 물이 담긴 접시가 있습니다.

**9** 이제, 저는 접시 한가운데에 초를 놓을 것입니다.

**10** 그다음에 초를 켜고 유리컵으로 초를 덮어 보겠습니다. "아브라카다브라!"

**11** 지나: 물을 보세요! 어째서 물이 유리컵 속으로 올라간 거지요?

**12** Ken: 공기가 뜨거워지면 팽창해서, 더 높은 압력을 만듭니다.

**13** 공기가 차가워지면 수축해서, 더 낮은 압력을 만듭니다.

**14** 불꽃이 다 타 버렸을 때, 유리컵 속의 공기는 식어 버렸습니다.

**15** 공기가 식었으므로, 기압이 낮아졌습니다.

**16** So the air _____ the glass _____ _____ _____ _____
_____.

**17** It _____ the water _____ the glass.

**18** Ken: Now, I'm _____ _____ _____ _____
_____ _____ _____ water.

**19** I will move _____ _____ _____ _____ you.

**20** Jina, _____ _____ has the water in it?

**21** Jina: That's easy! _____ the _____ _____.

**22** Ken: Okay, _____ _____. See? No water.

**23** Jina: Show _____ _____ _____ _____.

**24** Ken: See? There's _____ _____.

**25** Jina: Wow! _____ _____ the water _____?

**26** Ken: _____ the trick, I _____ a special material _____
_____ _____ _____ _____ _____.

**27** The material _____ the water and _____ _____ _____
jelly.

**28** Then the jelly _____ _____ _____ _____.

**29** If you _____ _____ _____ this trick, it's _____
_____ _____ cups _____ you can't _____ _____.

**30** Jina: Thank you _____ your great _____. It was really
_____!

16 그래서 유리컵 밖의 공기 압력이 더 높아졌습니다.

17 높아진 압력의 공기가 물을 밀어서 유리컵으로 들어가게 된 것입니다.

18 Ken: 이제, 이 컵들 중 하나를 물로 채워 보겠습니다.

19 여러분을 헷갈리게 하려고 이 컵들을 섞어 보겠습니다.

20 지나, 어떤 컵에 물이 있을까요?

21 지나: 쉽네요! 가운데 컵이에요.

22 Ken: 좋습니다. 확인해 봅시다. 보셨죠? 물이 없군요.

23 지나: 다른 컵들도 보여 주세요.

24 Ken: 보셨죠? 물이 없네요.

25 지나: 왜! 어째서 물이 사라진 거죠?

26 Ken: 마술 전에, 저는 특별한 물질을 컵 하나에 넣어 두었습니다.

27 그 물질은 물을 흡수하고, 그것을 젤리로 변하게 했습니다.

28 그리고 나서 젤리는 컵 바닥에 달라붙었습니다.

29 여러분이 이 마술을 해 보고자 한다면, 속을 들여다볼 수 없는 컵을 사용해야 합니다.

30 지나: 멋진 공연 고맙습니다. 정말 놀라웠어요!

※ 다음 문장을 우리말로 쓰시오.

**1** Jina: Welcome to the Super Science Magic Show!

➡ _____

**2** It's always exciting to see magic tricks.

➡ _____

**3** And it's more exciting to find out the secrets behind them.

➡ _____

**4** Some people think the secret of magic is science.

➡ _____

**5** Today, Ken, a member of the School Magic Club, will use science to perform his tricks.

➡ _____

**6** Which tricks will he show us? I can't wait to see them.

➡ _____

**7** Ken: Hello, everyone. Today, I'm going to show you something amazing.

➡ _____

**8** Here's a dish with water in it.

➡ _____

**9** Now, I'll put a candle in the middle of the dish.

➡ _____

**10** Next, I'll light the candle and cover it with a glass. "Abracadabra!"

➡ _____

**11** Jina: Look at the water! How come it rose into the glass?

➡ _____

**12** Ken: Air expands when it gets hot and creates higher pressure.

➡ _____

**13** When it gets cold, air contracts and creates lower pressure.

➡ _____

**14** When the flame burnt out, the air inside the glass cooled down.

➡ _____

**15** As the air cooled down, the air pressure dropped.

➡ _____

16▶ So the air outside the glass was at a higher pressure.

➡ _____

17▶ It pushed the water into the glass.

➡ _____

18▶ Ken: Now, I'm going to fill one of these cups with water.

➡ _____

19▶ I will move them around to confuse you.

➡ _____

20▶ Jina, which cup has the water in it?

➡ _____

21▶ Jina: That's easy! It's the middle one.

➡ _____

22▶ Ken: Okay, let's check. See? No water.

➡ _____

23▶ Jina: Show me the other cups.

➡ _____

24▶ Ken: See? There's no water.

➡ _____

25▶ Jina: Wow! How come the water disappeared?

➡ _____

26▶ Ken: Before the trick, I put a special material into one of the cups.

➡ _____

27▶ The material absorbed the water and turned it into jelly.

➡ _____

28▶ Then the jelly stuck to the bottom.

➡ _____

29▶ If you want to try this trick, it's necessary to use cups that you can't see through.

➡ _____

30▶ Jina: Thank you for your great performance. It was really amazing!

➡ _____

※ 다음 괄호 안의 단어들을 우리말에 맞도록 바르게 배열하시오.

**1** (Jina: / to / welcome / the / Science / Super / Show! / Magic)

➡ _____

**2** (always / it's / to / exciting / see / tricks. / magic)

➡ _____

**3** (it's / and / exciting / more / find / to / out / secrets / the / them. / behind)

➡ _____

**4** (people / some / the / think / of / secret / is / magic / science.)

➡ _____

**5** (Ken, / today, / member / a / of / School / the / Club, / Magic / use / will / to / science / perform / tricks. / his)

➡ _____

**6** (tricks / which / he / will / us? / show // I / wait / can't / see / them. / to)

➡ _____

**7** (Ken: / everyone. / hello, // today, / going / I'm / show / to / something / you / amazing.)

➡ _____

**8** (a / here's / with / dish / in / water / it.)

➡ _____

**9** (now, / put / I'll / candle / a / the / in / of / middle / dish. / the)

➡ _____

**10** (next, / light / I'll / candle / the / and / it / cover / with / glass. / a // "Abracadabra!")

➡ _____

**11** (Jina: / at / look / water! / the // come / how / rose / it / the / into / glass?)

➡ _____

**12** (Ken: / expands / air / it / when / gets / and / hot / higher / creates / pressure.)

➡ _____

**13** (it / when / cold, / gets / contracts / air / and / lower / creates / pressure.)

➡ _____

**14** (the / when / burnt / flame / out, / air / the / inside / glass / the / down. / cooled)

➡ _____

**15** (the / as / cooled / air / down, / air / the / dropped. / pressure)

➡ _____

1 지나: 특별 과학 마술 쇼에 오신 것을 환영합니다!

2 마술을 보는 것은 항상 신나는 일입니다.

3 그리고 마술 뒤에 숨겨진 비밀을 알아내는 것은 더 신나는 일입니다.

4 어떤 사람들은 마술의 비밀이 과학이라고 생각합니다.

5 오늘 학교 마술 동아리 회원인 Ken은 마술을 수행하기 위해 과학을 사용할 것입니다.

6 그는 우리에게 어떤 마술을 보여줄까요? 무척 기다려지는군요.

7 Ken: 안녕하세요, 여러분. 오늘, 저는 여러분에게 놀라운 무언가를 보여 주려고 합니다.

8 여기에 물이 담긴 접시가 있습니다.

9 이제, 저는 접시 한가운데에 초를 놓을 것입니다.

10 그다음에 초를 켜고 유리컵으로 초를 덮어 보겠습니다. "아브라카다브라!"

11 지나: 물을 보세요! 어째서 물이 유리컵 속으로 올라간 거지요?

12 Ken: 공기가 뜨거워지면 팽창해서, 더 높은 압력을 만듭니다.

13 공기가 차가워지면 수축해서, 더 낮은 압력을 만듭니다.

14 불꽃이 다 타 버렸을 때, 유리컵 속의 공기는 식어 버렸습니다.

15 공기가 식었으므로, 기압이 낮아졌습니다.

**16** (the / so / outside / air / glass / the / at / was / a / pressure. / higher)
➡ _____

**17** (pushed / it / water / the / the / glass. / into)
➡ _____

**18** (Ken: / now, / going / I'm / fill / to / of / one / cups / these / water. / with)
➡ _____

**19** (I / move / will / around / them / confuse / you. / to)
➡ _____

**20** (Jina, / cup / which / the / has / in / it? / water)
➡ _____

**21** (Jina: / easy! / that's // the / it's / one. / middle)
➡ _____

**22** (Ken: / okay, / check. / let's // see? // water. / no)
➡ _____

**23** (Jina: / me / show / other / the / cups.)
➡ _____

**24** (Ken: / see? // no / there's / water.)
➡ _____

**25** (Jina: / wow! // come / how / water / the / disappeared?)
➡ _____

**26** (Ken: / the / before / trick, / put / I / a / material / special / one / into / cups. / the / of)
➡ _____

**27** (material / the / absorbed / water / the / and / it / turned / jelly. / into)
➡ _____

**28** (the / then / stuck / jelly / to / bottom. / the)
➡ _____

**29** (you / if / to / want / try / trick, / this / necessary / it's / use / to / cups / you / that / see / can't / through.)
➡ _____
➡ _____

**30** (Jina: / you / thank / your / for / performance. / great // was / it / amazing! / really)
➡ _____

16 그래서 유리컵 밖의 공기 압력이 더 높아졌습니다.

17 높아진 압력의 공기가 물을 밀어서 유리컵으로 들어가게 된 것입니다.

18 Ken: 이제, 이 컵들 중 하나를 물로 채워 보겠습니다.

19 여러분을 헷갈리게 하려고 이 컵들을 섞어 보겠습니다.

20 지나, 어떤 컵에 물이 있을까요?

21 지나: 쉽네요! 가운데 컵이에요.

22 Ken: 좋습니다. 확인해 봅시다. 보셨죠? 물이 없군요.

23 지나: 다른 컵들도 보여 주세요.

24 Ken: 보셨죠? 물이 없네요.

25 지나: 왜 어째서 물이 사라진 거죠?

26 Ken: 마술 전에, 저는 특별한 물질을 컵 하나에 넣어 두었습니다.

27 그 물질은 물을 흡수하고, 그것을 젤리로 변하게 했습니다.

28 그리고 나서 젤리는 컵 바닥에 달라붙었습니다.

29 여러분이 이 마술을 해 보고자 한다면, 속을 들여다볼 수 없는 컵을 사용해야 합니다.

30 지나: 멋진 공연 고맙습니다. 정말 놀라웠어요!

※ 다음 우리말을 영어로 쓰시오.

**1** 지나: 특별 과학 마술 쇼에 오신 것을 환영합니다!

➡ _____

**2** 마술을 보는 것은 항상 신나는 일입니다.

➡ _____

**3** 그리고 마술 뒤에 숨겨진 비밀을 알아내는 것은 더 신나는 일입니다.

➡ _____

**4** 어떤 사람들은 마술의 비밀이 과학이라고 생각합니다.

➡ _____

**5** 오늘 학교 마술 동아리 회원인 Ken은 마술을 수행하기 위해 과학을 사용할 것입니다.

➡ _____

**6** 그는 우리에게 어떤 마술을 보여 줄까요? 무척 기다려지는군요.

➡ _____

**7** Ken: 안녕하세요, 여러분. 오늘, 저는 여러분에게 놀라운 무언가를 보여 주려고 합니다.

➡ _____

**8** 여기에 물이 담긴 접시가 있습니다.

➡ _____

**9** 이제, 저는 접시 한가운데에 초를 놓을 것입니다.

➡ _____

**10** 그다음에 초를 켜고 유리컵으로 초를 덮어 보겠습니다. "아브라카다브라!"

➡ _____

**11** 지나: 물을 보세요! 어째서 물이 유리컵 속으로 올라간 거지요?

➡ _____

**12** Ken: 공기가 뜨거워지면 팽창해서, 더 높은 압력을 만듭니다.

➡ _____

**13** 공기가 차가워지면 수축해서, 더 낮은 압력을 만듭니다.

➡ _____

**14** 불꽃이 다 타 버렸을 때, 유리컵 속의 공기는 식어 버렸습니다.

➡ _____

**15** 공기가 식었으므로, 기압이 낮아졌습니다.

➡ _____

**16** 그래서 유리컵 밖의 공기 압력이 더 높아졌습니다.

➡ _____

**17** 높아진 압력의 공기가 물을 밀어서 유리컵으로 들어가게 된 것입니다.

➡ _____

**18** Ken: 이제, 이 컵들 중 하나를 물로 채워 보겠습니다.

➡ _____

**19** 여러분을 헷갈리게 하려고 이 컵들을 섞어 보겠습니다.

➡ _____

**20** 지나, 어떤 컵에 물이 있을까요?

➡ _____

**21** 지나: 쉽네요! 가운데 컵이에요.

➡ _____

**22** Ken: 좋습니다, 확인해 봅시다. 보셨죠? 물이 없군요.

➡ _____

**23** 지나: 다른 컵들도 보여 주세요.

➡ _____

**24** Ken: 보셨죠? 물이 없네요.

➡ _____

**25** 지나: 와! 어째서 물이 사라진 거죠?

➡ _____

**26** Ken: 마술 전에, 저는 특별한 물질을 컵 하나에 넣어 두었습니다.

➡ _____

**27** 그 물질은 물을 흡수하고, 그것을 젤리로 변하게 했습니다.

➡ _____

**28** 그리고 나서 젤리는 컵 바닥에 달라붙었습니다.

➡ _____

**29** 여러분이 이 마술을 해 보고자 한다면, 속을 들여다볼 수 없는 컵을 사용해야 합니다.

➡ _____

**30** 지나: 멋진 공연 고맙습니다. 정말 놀라웠어요!

➡ _____

※ 다음 우리말과 일치하도록 빈칸에 알맞은 말을 쓰시오.

### Real Life Communication B

1. A: _____ _____ do you want to _____ _____ _____?

2. B: I want to _____ the badminton _____. I _____ _____ badminton. How _____ you?

3. A: I want to _____ _____ _____ _____. I _____ _____ make a computer program there.

4. B: That _____ cool!

1. A: 무슨 수업을 등록하고 싶니?
2. B: 난 배드민턴 수업을 듣고 싶어. 나는 배드민턴 치는 것을 좋아하거든. 너는?
3. A: 난 컴퓨터 수업을 듣고 싶어. 나는 빨리 거기에서 컴퓨터 프로그램을 만들고 싶어.
4. B: 맛진 것 같아!

### Culture & Life

1. North _____ _____ – The Bermuda _____

2. _____ _____ _____ airplanes and ships _____ _____ in the Bermuda Triangle.

3. How _____?

4. It's _____ a mystery.

1. 북대서양 – 버뮤다 삼각 지대
2. 많은 비행기와 선박이 버뮤다 삼각 지대에서 사라졌다.
3. 이유가 무엇일까?
4. 그것은 여전히 미스터리이다.

### Culture & Life

1. _____ – The pyramids

2. Some of the rocks _____ _____ _____ _____ the pyramids _____ _____ 70 tons.

3. How was _____ _____ _____ _____ such heavy rocks back then?

4. It's _____ _____ _____.

1. 이집트 – 피라미드
2. 피라미드를 만드는 데 사용된 몇몇 바위들은 무게가 70톤 정도인 것들이 있다.
3. 어떻게 그 시대에 그렇게 무거운 바위를 옮기는 것이 가능했을까?
4. 그것은 여전히 미스터리이다.

※ 다음 우리말을 영어로 쓰시오.

**Real Life Communication B**

1. A: 무슨 수업을 등록하고 싶니?
   ➡ _____

2. B: 난 배드민턴 수업을 듣고 싶어. 나는 배드민턴 치는 것을 좋아하거든. 너는?
   ➡ _____

3. A: 난 컴퓨터 수업을 듣고 싶어. 나는 빨리 거기에서 컴퓨터 프로그램을 만들고 싶어.
   ➡ _____

4. B: 멋진 것 같다!
   ➡ _____

**Culture & Life**

1. 북대서양 – 버뮤다 삼각 지대
   ➡ _____

2. 많은 비행기와 선박이 버뮤다 삼각 지대에서 사라졌다.
   ➡ _____

3. 이유가 무엇일까?
   ➡ _____

4. 그것은 여전히 미스터리이다.
   ➡ _____

**Culture & Life**

1. 이집트 – 피라미드
   ➡ _____

2. 피라미드를 만드는 데 사용된 몇몇 바위들은 무게가 70톤 정도인 것들이 있다.
   ➡ _____

3. 어떻게 그 시대에 그렇게 무거운 바위를 옮기는 것이 가능했을까?
   ➡ _____

4. 그것은 여전히 미스터리이다.
   ➡ _____

※ 다음 영어를 우리말로 쓰시오.

| | |
|---|---|
| 01 slippery | |
| 02 wide | |
| 03 bare | |
| 04 everywhere | |
| 05 village | |
| 06 shaky | |
| 07 ugly | |
| 08 excellent | |
| 09 experience | |
| 10 care | |
| 11 floating | |
| 12 gather | |
| 13 healthy | |
| 14 against | |
| 15 impossible | |
| 16 courage | |
| 17 match | |
| 18 meal | |
| 19 achievement | |
| 20 nail | |
| 21 exercise | |

| | |
|---|---|
| 22 proud | |
| 23 semi-final | |
| 24 discouraged | |
| 25 weak | |
| 26 amazing | |
| 27 shout | |
| 28 although | |
| 29 tournament | |
| 30 villager | |
| 31 completely | |
| 32 lose | |
| 33 decide | |
| 34 windy | |
| 35 fall into | |
| 36 try[do] one's best | |
| 37 on foot | |
| 38 try out for | |
| 39 give it a try | |
| 40 in fact | |
| 41 be about to | |
| 42 give up | |
| 43 laugh at | |

※ 다음 우리말을 영어로 쓰시오.

01 소리 지르다 _____

02 비록 ~일지라도 _____

03 걱정하다, 관심을 갖다 _____

04 흔들리는, 휘청거리는 _____

05 완전히 _____

06 낙담한 _____

07 미끄러운 _____

08 결정하다 _____

09 못질하다; 못 _____

10 모든 곳에, 어디나 _____

11 넓은 _____

12 경험하다 _____

13 떠 있는 _____

14 성과 _____

15 훌륭한 _____

16 ~에 맞서 _____

17 모으다, 모이다 _____

18 경기 _____

19 건강한 _____

20 숯하다 _____

21 약한 _____

22 벌거벗은, 맨 ~ _____

23 불가능한 _____

24 마을 사람 _____

25 지다, 잃다 _____

26 용기 _____

27 놀라운 _____

28 바람이 센 _____

29 식사, 끼니 _____

30 못생긴, 추한 _____

31 자랑스러워하는 _____

32 준결승전 _____

33 운동하다 _____

34 씻다 _____

35 사실은 _____

36 걸어서, 도보로 _____

37 시도해 보다 _____

38 ~을 비웃다 _____

39 최선을 다하다 _____

40 포기하다 _____

41 막 ~하려고 하다 _____

42 ~에 빠지다 _____

43 ~을 잘하다 _____

※ 다음 영영풀이에 알맞은 단어를 <보기>에서 골라 쓴 후, 우리말 뜻을 쓰시오.

1 _____ : extremely good: _____

2 _____ : not physically strong: _____

3 _____ : to fail to win a game: _____

4 _____ : not covered by clothes: _____

5 _____ : to say something very loudly: _____

6 _____ : someone who lives in a village: _____

7 _____ : not firm or steady: _____

8 _____ : a contest between two or more players or teams: _____

9 _____ : to fasten something to something else with nails: _____

10 _____ : a thing done successfully, typically by effort, courage, or skill:
_____

11 _____ : to get things from different places and put them together in one place:
_____

12 _____ : no longer having the confidence you need to continue doing something:
_____

13 _____ : feeling pleased about something that you have done or something that you
own: _____

14 _____ : difficult to hold or to stand or move on, because it is smooth, wet or
polished: _____

15 _____ : the quality of being brave when you are facing a difficult or dangerous
situation, or when you are very ill: _____

16 _____ : to kick or throw a ball in a sport such as football or basketball towards
the place where you can get a point: _____

보기

| | | | |
|---|---|---|---|
| shoot | gather | achievement | discouraged |
| nail | lose | match | villager |
| weak | excellent | slippery | shout |
| courage | bare | shaky | proud |

※ 다음 우리말과 일치하도록 빈칸에 알맞은 말을 쓰시오.

**Listen & Speak 1 A**

G: Tim, _____ _____ _____ _____ the Gobi Desert?

B: Yes, I _____. _____ it _____ Mongolia and China?

G: Yes, it is. Yesterday, I _____ a TV show about people _____ _____ the desert _____ _____.

B: _____ on foot?

G: Yes, it _____ them _____ 51 days.

B: Wow, that's amazing. I want _____ _____ _____ in the _____ but I don't want to _____ it _____ _____.

G: Well, I want to _____ and _____ the Gobi Desert _____ 50 days.

**Listen & Speak 1 B**

G: Alex, _____ _____ _____ _____ _____ this year's "Ugly Sweater Party?"

B: Of _____, I _____. It's _____ December 5th, _____?

G: That's _____. Are you _____ _____ go?

B: I _____ _____, but I don't have an ugly sweater.

G: I have one that _____ _____ _____ _____ _____. You can have it _____ _____ _____.

B: Thanks. That _____ be great.

G: _____ _____ _____ _____ _____ the Student Center and _____ _____ together.

B: _____. _____ you then.

**Listen & Speak 2 A**

W: What can you do to be _____? First, try to _____ every day. Second, _____ _____ _____ _____ _____ _____. _____ _____ too much fast food. Third, _____ your hands before _____. Do these tips _____ _____ to do? Well, _____ one _____ _____ _____ _____ and don't _____ _____. Then you'll _____ a healthy _____.

G: Tim, 너는 고비 사막에 대해 들어 봤니?
B: 응, 들어 봤어. 그것은 몽골과 중국에 있지 않니?
G: 응, 맞아. 어제 나는 걸어서 그 사막을 건넌 사람들에 관한 TV 쇼를 봤어.
B: 단지 걸어서만?
G: 응, 51일 정도 걸렸어.
B: 와, 놀랍다. 나는 사막에서의 삶을 경험하고 싶지만 그곳을 걸어서 건너고 싶지는 않아.
G: 음, 나는 시도해 보고 싶고 고비 사막을 50일 내로 건너고 싶어.

G: Alex, 너는 올해의 "못생긴 스웨터 파티"에 대해 들어 봤니?
B: 물론 들어 봤어. 그것은 12월 5일에 열려, 맞지?
G: 맞아. 너 갈 거니?
B: 가고 싶지만 나는 못생긴 스웨터가 없어.
G: 집에 내가 입지 않는 스웨터가 한 벌 있어. 네가 원하면 그걸 가져도 좋아.
B: 고마워. 그래주면 좋겠어.
G: 학생회관 앞에서 만나서 같이 들어가자.
B: 그래. 그때 보자.

W: 당신은 건강해지기 위해 무엇을 할 수 있는가? 먼저, 매일 운동하도록 해라. 둘째, 건강에 좋은 음식을 먹도록 해라. 패스트푸드를 너무 많이 먹지 마라. 셋째, 식사 전에 손을 씻어라. 이 조언들이 실천하기에 어렵게 들리는가? 음, 한 번에 하나씩 행하고 포기하지 마라. 그러면 당신은 건강한 삶을 살 것이다.

### Listen & Speak 2 B

G: Hojun, are you going to _____ _____ _____ the school ice hockey team? The new season _____ _____ _____ start.

B: I'm not _____.

G: _____ _____?

B: I _____ that Tony and Brad are also _____ _____ _____ the team. They're so good.

G: Well, you're also _____ _____ ice hockey, so _____ _____ _____!

B: Okay, I'll _____ _____ _____. Thanks _____ _____.

G: 호준아, 너 학교 아이스하키 팀에 지원할 예정이니? 새 시즌이 곧 시작돼.
B: 잘 모르겠어.
G: 왜 몰라?
B: Tony와 Brad도 그 팀에 지원할 거라고 들었어. 그들은 굉장히 잘해.
G: 음, 너 또한 아이스하키를 잘하잖아, 그러니 포기하지 마!
B: 알았어, 최선을 다할게. 정말 고마워.

### Real Life Communication

Father: Emily, are you _____ about your _____ on Saturday?

Emily: Not really. We're playing _____ a strong team. I think we'll _____.

Father: _____ _____ that. _____ _____ _____ _____ the Greek team in the 2004 Euro Cup?

Emily: _____, I _____. What _____ them?

Father: They were a weak team, _____ everyone _____ that they would _____.

Emily: _____ _____?

Father: They played _____ a team and _____ _____. Finally, they _____ the Euro Cup. So, don't _____ _____.

Emily: Thanks, Dad. We'll _____ _____ _____.

Father: Emily, 토요일에 있을 경기에 대해 설레니?
Emily: 그렇진 않아요. 우리는 강한 팀에 맞서 시합할 거예요. 우리가 질 것 같아요.
Father: 그렇게 말하지 마. 너는 2004 유로컵에서 그리스 팀에 대해 들어 봤니?
Emily: 아니요, 들어본 적 없어요. 그들이 어땠는데요?
Father: 그들은 약한 팀이었어, 그래서 모두가 그들이 질 거라고 생각했지.
Emily: 무슨 일이 일어났는데요?
Father: 그들은 한 팀으로 경기하며 열심히 노력했어. 결국 그들은 유로컵에서 우승했단다. 그러니 포기하지 마.
Emily: 감사해요, 아빠. 우리도 최선을 다할게요.

### Let's Check ❶

B: _____ _____ _____ _____ Thomas Edison? _____ he was young, he _____ _____ _____. Also, he _____ all of the _____ _____ his left ear. _____, he became a great scientist. _____ you may have _____, _____ _____ _____ Edison and _____ _____ _____.

B: 당신은 Thomas Edison에 대해 들어 봤나요? 어렸을 때 그는 글을 잘 읽지 못했습니다. 또한 그는 왼쪽 귀가 전혀 들리지 않았습니다. 그럼에도 그는 위대한 과학자가 되었습니다. 당신이 어려움을 갖고 있을지라도, Edison처럼 되고 포기하지 마세요.

※ 다음 우리말에 맞도록 대화를 영어로 쓰시오.

### Listen & Speak 1 A

G: _____

B: _____

G: _____

_____

B: _____

G: _____

B: _____

_____

G: _____

### Listen & Speak 1 B

G: _____

B: _____

G: _____

B: _____

G: _____

B: _____

G: _____

B: _____

### Listen & Speak 2 A

W: _____

_____

_____

_____

G: Tim, 너는 고비 사막에 대해 들어 봤니?
B: 응, 들어 봤어. 그것은 몽골과 중국에 있지 않니?
G: 응, 맞아. 어제 나는 걸어서 그 사막을 건넌 사람들에 관한 TV 쇼를 봤어.
B: 단지 걸어서만?
G: 응, 51일 정도 걸렸어.
B: 와, 놀랍다. 나는 사막에서의 삶을 경험하고 싶지만 그곳을 걸어서 건너고 싶지는 않아.
G: 음, 나는 시도해 보고 싶고 고비 사막을 50일 내로 건너고 싶어.

G: Alex, 너는 올해의 "못생긴 스웨터 파티"에 대해 들어 봤니?
B: 물론 들어 봤어. 그것은 12월 5일에 열려, 맞지?
G: 맞아. 너 갈 거니?
B: 가고 싶지만 나는 못생긴 스웨터가 없어.
G: 집에 내가 입지 않는 스웨터가 한 벌 있어. 네가 원하면 그걸 가져도 좋아.
B: 고마워. 그래주면 좋겠어.
G: 학생회관 앞에서 만나서 같이 들어가자.
B: 그래. 그때 보자.

W: 당신은 건강해지기 위해 무엇을 할 수 있는가? 먼저, 매일 운동하도록 해라. 둘째, 건강에 좋은 음식을 먹도록 해라. 패스트푸드를 너무 많이 먹지 마라. 셋째, 식사 전에 손을 씻어라. 이 조언들이 실천하기에 어렵게 들리는가? 음, 한 번에 하나씩 행하고 포기하지 마라. 그러면 당신은 건강한 삶을 살 것이다.

### Listen & Speak 2 B

G: _____

_____

B: _____

G: _____

B: _____

G: _____

B: _____

### Real Life Communication

Father: _____

Emily: _____

Father: _____

Emily: _____

Father: _____

Emily: _____

Father: _____

Emily: _____

### Let's Check ❶

B: _____

_____

_____

_____

G: 호준아, 너 학교 아이스하키 팀에 지원할 예정이니? 새 시즌이 곧 시작돼.

B: 잘 모르겠어.

G: 왜 몰라?

B: Tony와 Brad도 그 팀에 지원할 거라고 들었어. 그들은 굉장히 잘해.

G: 음, 너 또한 아이스하키를 잘하잖아, 그러니 포기하지 마!

B: 알았어, 최선을 다할게. 정말 고마워.

Father: Emily, 토요일에 있을 경기에 대해 설레니?

Emily: 그렇진 않아요. 우리는 강한 팀에 맞서 시합할 거예요. 우리가 질 것 같아요.

Father: 그렇게 말하지 마. 너는 2004 유로컵에서 그리스 팀에 대해 들어 봤니?

Emily: 아니요, 들어본 적 없어요. 그들이 어땠는데요?

Father: 그들은 약한 팀이었어, 그래서 모두가 그들이 질 거라고 생각했지.

Emily: 무슨 일이 일어났는데요?

Father: 그들은 한 팀으로 경기하며 열심히 노력했어. 결국 그들은 유로컵에서 우승했단다. 그러니 포기하지 마.

Emily: 감사해요, 아빠. 우리도 최선을 다할게요.

B: 당신은 Thomas Edison에 대해 들어 봤나요? 어렸을 때 그는 글을 잘 읽지 못했습니다. 또한 그는 왼쪽 귀가 전혀 들리지 않았습니다. 그럼에도 그는 위대한 과학자가 되었습니다. 당신이 어려움을 갖고 있을지라도, Edison처럼 되고 포기하지 마세요.

※ 다음 우리말과 일치하도록 빈칸에 알맞은 것을 골라 쓰시오.

**1** Koh Panyee was a small _____ _____ in the _____ of the sea.

A. village        B. floating        C. middle

**2** _____ the boys in the village _____ _____ soccer before, they loved _____ it on TV.

A. never        B. watching        C. played        D. although

**3** One day, the boys _____ _____ _____ their _____ soccer team.

A. own        B. decided        C. make        D. to

**4** _____, people _____ _____ their idea.

A. laughed        B. at        C. however

**5** "_____ _____."

A. impossible        B. that's

**6** "What _____ you _____ _____?"

A. say        B. makes        C. so

**7** "_____ _____. Where are you _____ to _____ soccer?"

A. going        B. around        C. look        D. play

**8** The _____ were _____. The boys had no _____ _____ play soccer.

A. right        B. place        C. to        D. villagers

**9** They _____ _____.

A. discouraged        B. were

**10** "Don't _____ _____! We can _____ _____ soccer."

A. up        B. still        C. give        D. play

**11** "How?"

**12** "_____ make our _____ soccer _____."

A. field        B. own        C. let's

**13** The boys _____ old boats and _____ _____ wood.

A. pieces        B. gathered        C. of

**14** They _____ the boats _____ and _____ the wood _____ them.

A. together        B. to        C. put        D. nailed

**15** _____ much hard _____, they _____ had a _____ field.

A. work        B. after        C. floating        D. finally

**16** It was _____ and had _____ _____.

A. nails        B. shaky        C. everywhere

---

1 Koh Panyee는 바다 가운데 떠 있는 작은 수상 마을이었다.

2 비록 그 마을의 소년들은 이전에 축구를 해 본 적이 없었지만, 그들은 그것을 TV로 보는 것을 정말 좋아했다.

3 어느 날, 그 소년들은 그들만의 축구팀을 만들기로 하였다.

4 그러나 사람들은 그들의 생각을 비웃었다.

5 "그것은 불가능해."

6 "왜 그렇게 말하는 거죠?"

7 "주위를 둘러봐. 너희는 어디서 축구를 할 거니?"

8 마을 사람들이 옳았다. 소년들은 축구를 할 장소가 없었다.

9 그들은 낙담했다.

10 "포기하지 마! 우리는 여전히 축구를 할 수 있어."

11 "어떻게?"

12 "우리만의 축구장을 만들자."

13 소년들은 낡은 배와 나뭇조각들을 모았다.

14 그들은 배를 합치고 그것들 위에 나무를 못으로 박았다.

15 매우 열심히 일한 후, 그들은 마침내 떠 있는 축구장을 가지게 되었다.

16 그것은 흔들리고 곳곳에 못이 있었다.

---

**17** The ball and the boys would often _____ the sea, so the field was always _____ and _____.

A. into          B. slippery          C. wet          D. fall

**18** They had _____ _____ so they had to play in _____.

A. bare          B. shoes          C. no          D. feet

**19** _____, they didn't _____.

A. care          B. still

**20** _____ _____, they built _____ skills and _____ playing soccer more.

A. fact          B. enjoyed          C. excellent          D. in

**21** _____ day, a boy _____ a _____ about a soccer _____.

A. brought          B. one          C. tournament          D. poster

**22** They _____ _____ give _____ a _____.

A. decided          B. to          C. try          D. it

**23** _____ they were _____ to _____, the villagers gave them new _____ and uniforms.

A. leave          B. about          C. when          D. shoes

**24** Some _____ came to watch the game. This _____ the boys _____ _____.

A. made          B. better          C. feel          D. even

**25** _____ first, people _____ them _____ the _____ team.

A. weakest          B. at          C. as          D. saw

**26** _____, when the tournament _____, the soccer team _____ everyone.

A. surprised          B. however          C. started

**27** _____ the day of the _____, it was _____ _____.

A. raining          B. on          C. hard          D. semi-final

**28** They were _____ _____ two goals and it looked _____ to _____.

A. by          B. win          C. impossible          D. losing

**29** "The _____ team is so _____," they _____.

A. strong          B. other          C. thought

**30** But the boys _____ _____ _____.

A. up          B. give          C. didn't

**31** They _____ _____ their shoes _____ the second half and the game changed _____.

A. during          B. off          C. completely          D. took

**32** They played _____ in the rain _____ _____ the _____ field at home.

A. to          B. slippery          C. thanks          D. better

**33** Although they lost _____ a score of three _____ two, still, they felt _____ _____ themselves.

A. of          B. by          C. to          D. proud

**34** They didn't _____ up when they were _____. They _____ their best _____ the end.

A. tried          B. give          C. until          D. losing

**17** 공과 소년들은 종종 바다에 빠졌고, 축구장은 항상 젖어 있고 미끄러웠다.

**18** 그들은 신발이 없어서 맨발로 축구를 해야 했다.

**19** 그런데도 그들은 상관하지 않았다.

**20** 실제로 그들은 훌륭한 기술을 쌓았고 더욱 더 축구를 즐겼다.

**21** 어느 날, 한 소년이 축구 토너먼트에 관한 포스터를 가지고 왔다.

**22** 그들은 한번 해 보기로 결정했다.

**23** 그들이 떠나려고 할 때, 마을 사람들은 그들에게 새 신발과 축구복을 주었다.

**24** 몇몇은 심지어 경기를 보러 왔다. 이것은 소년들의 기분을 더 좋게 만들었다.

**25** 처음에, 사람들은 그들을 가장 약한 팀으로 보았다.

**26** 그러나 토너먼트가 시작되었을 때, 그 축구팀은 모든 사람들을 놀라게 했다.

**27** 준결승전 날, 비가 심하게 오고 있었다.

**28** 그들은 두 골 차로 지고 있었고, 이기는 것은 불가능해 보였다.

**29** "다른 팀이 아주 강해."라고 그들은 생각했다.

**30** 그러나 소년들은 포기하지 않았다.

**31** 그들은 후반전에 그들의 신발을 벗었고 경기는 완전히 바뀌었다.

**32** 고향의 미끄러운 축구장 덕분에 그들은 빗속에서 더 잘하였다.

**33** 비록 그들은 3대 2로 졌지만, 그들은 그들 자신이 자랑스러웠다.

**34** 그들은 그들이 지고 있을 때 포기하지 않았다. 그들은 끝까지 최선을 다하였다.

※ 다음 우리말과 일치하도록 빈칸에 알맞은 말을 쓰시오.

**1** Koh Panyee was _____ _____ _____ _____ in the _____ of the sea.

**2** _____ the boys in the village _____ _____ _____ before, they loved _____ _____ _____ _____ .

**3** _____ _____ , the boys _____ _____ _____ their own soccer team.

**4** _____ , people _____ _____ _____ _____ .

**5** "That's _____ ."

**6** "What _____ you _____ _____ ?"

**7** " _____ _____ . Where _____ you _____ _____ _____ soccer?"

**8** The villagers _____ _____ . The boys had _____ _____ _____ _____ .

**9** They _____ _____ .

**10** "Don't _____ _____ ! We can _____ _____ _____ ."

**11** " _____ ?"

**12** " _____ _____ _____ _____ _____ soccer field."

**13** The boys _____ old boats and _____ _____ _____ .

**14** They _____ the boats _____ and _____ the wood _____ them.

**15** _____ _____ hard work, they _____ _____ _____ _____ .

**16** It was _____ and _____ _____ _____ .

**1** Koh Panyee는 바다 가운데 떠 있는 작은 수상 마을이었다.

**2** 비록 그 마을의 소년들은 이전에 축구를 해 본 적이 없었지만, 그들은 그것을 TV로 보는 것을 정말 좋아했다.

**3** 어느 날, 그 소년들은 그들만의 축구팀을 만들기로 하였다.

**4** 그러나 사람들은 그들의 생각을 비웃었다.

**5** "그것은 불가능해."

**6** "왜 그렇게 말하는 거죠?"

**7** "주위를 둘러봐. 너희는 어디서 축구를 할 거니?"

**8** 마을 사람들이 옳았다. 소년들은 축구를 할 장소가 없었다.

**9** 그들은 낙담했다.

**10** "포기하지 마! 우리는 여전히 축구를 할 수 있어."

**11** "어떻게?"

**12** "우리만의 축구장을 만들자."

**13** 소년들은 낡은 배와 나뭇조각들을 모았다.

**14** 그들은 배를 합치고 그것들 위에 나무를 못으로 박았다.

**15** 매우 열심히 일한 후, 그들은 마침내 떠 있는 축구장을 가지게 되었다.

**16** 그것은 흔들리고 곳곳에 못이 있었다.

**17** The ball and the boys _____ _____ _____ the sea, so the field was _____ _____ and _____.

**18** They had _____ _____ so they _____ _____ play in _____ _____.

**19** _____, _____ didn't _____.

**20** _____ _____, they built _____ skills and _____ _____ soccer more.

**21** One day, a boy _____ _____ _____ about a soccer tournament.

**22** They _____ _____ give _____ a _____.

**23** _____ they _____ _____ _____ _____, the villagers gave _____ _____ and uniforms.

**24** Some even came to watch the game. This _____ the boys _____ _____.

**25** At first, people _____ them _____ the _____ team.

**26** _____, _____ the tournament _____, the soccer team _____ _____.

**27** _____ the day of the semi-final, it _____ _____ _____.

**28** They were _____ _____ _____ _____ and it looked _____ _____ _____.

**29** "_____ team is _____ _____," they thought.

**30** _____ the boys didn't _____ _____.

**31** They _____ _____ their shoes _____ the _____ _____ and the game _____ _____.

**32** They _____ _____ in the rain _____ the slippery field at home.

**33** _____ they _____ _____ _____ a score of three _____ two, still, they felt _____ _____.

**34** They didn't _____ _____ _____ _____ _____ _____. They _____ _____ _____ until the end.

**17** 공과 소년들은 종종 바다에 빠졌고, 축구장은 항상 젖어 있고 미끄러웠다.

**18** 그들은 신발이 없어서 맨발로 축구를 해야 했다.

**19** 그런데도 그들은 상관하지 않았다.

**20** 실제로 그들은 훌륭한 기술을 쌓았고 더욱 더 축구를 즐겼다.

**21** 어느 날, 한 소년이 축구 토너먼트에 관한 포스터를 가지고 왔다.

**22** 그들은 한번 해 보기로 결정했다.

**23** 그들이 떠나려고 할 때, 마을 사람들은 그들에게 새 신발과 축구복을 주었다.

**24** 몇몇은 심지어 경기를 보러 왔다. 이것은 소년들의 기분을 더 좋게 만들었다.

**25** 처음에, 사람들은 그들을 가장 약한 팀으로 보았다.

**26** 그러나 토너먼트가 시작되었을 때, 그 축구팀은 모든 사람들을 놀라게 했다.

**27** 준결승전 날, 비가 심하게 오고 있었다.

**28** 그들은 두 골 차로 지고 있었고, 이기는 것은 불가능해 보였다.

**29** "다른 팀이 아주 강해."라고 그들은 생각했다.

**30** 그러나 소년들은 포기하지 않았다.

**31** 그들은 후반전에 그들의 신발을 벗었고 경기는 완전히 바뀌었다.

**32** 고향의 미끄러운 축구장 덕분에 그들은 빗속에서 더 잘하였다.

**33** 비록 그들은 3대 2로 졌지만, 그들은 그들 자신이 자랑스러웠다.

**34** 그들은 그들이 지고 있을 때 포기하지 않았다. 그들은 끝까지 최선을 다하였다.

※ 다음 문장을 우리말로 쓰시오.

**1** Koh Panyee was a small floating village in the middle of the sea.

➡ _____

**2** Although the boys in the village never played soccer before, they loved watching it on TV.

➡ _____

**3** One day, the boys decided to make their own soccer team.

➡ _____

**4** However, people laughed at their idea.

➡ _____

**5** "That's impossible."

➡ _____

**6** "What makes you say so?"

➡ _____

**7** "Look around. Where are you going to play soccer?"

➡ _____

**8** The villagers were right. The boys had no place to play soccer.

➡ _____

**9** They were discouraged.

➡ _____

**10** "Don't give up! We can still play soccer."

➡ _____

**11** "How?"

➡ _____

**12** "Let's make our own soccer field."

➡ _____

**13** The boys gathered old boats and pieces of wood.

➡ _____

**14** They put the boats together and nailed the wood to them.

➡ _____

**15** After much hard work, they finally had a floating field.

➡ _____

**16** It was shaky and had nails everywhere.

➡ _____

**17** The ball and the boys would often fall into the sea, so the field was always wet and slippery.

➡ _____

**18** They had no shoes so they had to play in bare feet.

➡ _____

**19** Still, they didn't care.

➡ _____

**20** In fact, they built excellent skills and enjoyed playing soccer more.

➡ _____

**21** One day, a boy brought a poster about a soccer tournament.

➡ _____

**22** They decided to give it a try.

➡ _____

**23** When they were about to leave, the villagers gave them new shoes and uniforms.

➡ _____

**24** Some even came to watch the game. This made the boys feel better.

➡ _____

**25** At first, people saw them as the weakest team.

➡ _____

**26** However, when the tournament started, the soccer team surprised everyone.

➡ _____

**27** On the day of the semi-final, it was raining hard.

➡ _____

**28** They were losing by two goals and it looked impossible to win.

➡ _____

**29** "The other team is so strong," they thought.

➡ _____

**30** But the boys didn't give up.

➡ _____

**31** They took off their shoes during the second half and the game changed completely.

➡ _____

**32** They played better in the rain thanks to the slippery field at home.

➡ _____

**33** Although they lost by a score of three to two, still, they felt proud of themselves.

➡ _____

**34** They didn't give up when they were losing. They tried their best until the end.

➡ _____

※ 다음 괄호 안의 단어들을 우리말에 맞도록 바르게 배열하시오.

1 (Panyee / Koh / was / small / a / floating / village / the / in / middle / the / of / sea.)
➡ _____

2 (the / although / boys / in / village / the / played / never / before, / soccer / loved / they / it / watching / TV. / on)
➡ _____

3 (day, / one / boys / the / to / decided / make / own / their / team. / soccer)
➡ _____

4 (people / however, / at / laughed / idea. / their)
➡ _____

5 (impossible." / "that's)
➡ _____

6 (makes / "what / say / you / so?")
➡ _____

7 (around. / "look // are / where / going / you / soccer?" / play / to)
➡ _____

8 (villagers / the / right. / were // boys / the / no / had / to / place / soccer. / play)
➡ _____

9 (discouraged. / were / they)
➡ _____

10 (give / "don't / up! // can / we / play / still / soccer.")
➡ _____

11 ("how?")
➡ _____

12 (make / "let's / own / our / field." / soccer)
➡ _____

13 (boys / the / gathered / boats / old / and / wood. / of / pieces)
➡ _____

14 (put / they / boats / the / together / and / the / nailed / wood / them. / to)
➡ _____

15 (much / after / work, / hard / they / had / finally / a / field. / floating)
➡ _____

16 (was / it / shaky / and / nails / had / everywhere.)
➡ _____

1 Koh Panyee는 바다 가운데 떠 있는 작은 수상 마을이었다.

2 비록 그 마을의 소년들은 이전에 축구를 해 본 적이 없었지만, 그들은 그것을 TV로 보는 것을 정말 좋아했다.

3 어느 날, 그 소년들은 그들만의 축구팀을 만들기로 하였다.

4 그러나 사람들은 그들의 생각을 비웃었다.

5 "그것은 불가능해."

6 "왜 그렇게 말하는 거죠?"

7 "주위를 둘러봐. 너희는 어디서 축구를 할 거니?"

8 마을 사람들이 옳았다. 소년들은 축구를 할 장소가 없었다.

9 그들은 낙담했다.

10 "포기하지 마! 우리는 여전히 축구를 할 수 있어."

11 "어떻게?"

12 "우리만의 축구장을 만들자."

13 소년들은 낡은 배와 나뭇조각들을 모았다.

14 그들은 배를 합치고 그것들 위에 나무를 못으로 박았다.

15 매우 열심히 일한 후, 그들은 마침내 떠 있는 축구장을 가지게 되었다.

16 그것은 흔들리고 곳곳에 못이 있었다.

**17** (ball / the / and / boys / the / often / would / fall / into / sea, / the / so / field / the / always / was / slippery. / and / wet)
➡ _____

**18** (had / no / they / shoes / they / so / had / play / to / in / feet. / bare)
➡ _____

**19** (they / still, / care. / didn't)
➡ _____

**20** (fact, / in / built / they / skills / excellent / and / playing / enjoyed / more. / soccer)
➡ _____

**21** (day, / one / boy / a / brought / poster / a / about / soccer / a / tournament.)
➡ _____

**22** (decided / they / give / to / try. / a / it)
➡ _____

**23** (they / when / about / were / leave, / to / villagers / the / them / gave / shoes / new / uniforms. / and)
➡ _____

**24** (even / some / to / came / watch / game. / the // this / the / made / boys / better. / feel)
➡ _____

**25** (first, / at / saw / people / them / the / as / team. / weakest)
➡ _____

**26** (however, / the / when / started, / tournament / soccer / the / team / everyone. / surprised)
➡ _____

**27** (the / on / day / the / of / semi-final, / was / it / hard. / raining)
➡ _____

**28** (they / losing / were / two / by / goals / and / looked / it / to / impossible / win.)
➡ _____

**29** ("the / team / other / so / is / strong" / thought. / they)
➡ _____

**30** (But / boys / the / give / didn't / up.)
➡ _____

**31** (took / they / off / shoes / their / the / during / half / second / and / game / changed / the / completely.)
➡ _____

**32** (played / they / better / the / in / thanks / rain / to / field / the / slippery / home. / at)
➡ _____

**33** (they / although / by / lost / score / a / three / of / two, / to / still, / felt / they / proud / themselves. / of)
➡ _____

**34** (didn't / they / up / give / they / when / losing. / were // tried / they / best / their / until / end. / the)
➡ _____

**17** 공과 소년들은 종종 바다에 빠졌고, 축구장은 항상 젖어 있고 미끄러웠다.

**18** 그들은 신발이 없어서 맨발로 축구를 해야 했다.

**19** 그런데도 그들은 상관하지 않았다.

**20** 실제로 그들은 훌륭한 기술을 쌓았고 더욱 더 축구를 즐겼다.

**21** 어느 날, 한 소년이 축구 토너먼트에 관한 포스터를 가지고 왔다.

**22** 그들은 한번 해 보기로 결정했다.

**23** 그들이 떠나려고 할 때, 마을 사람들은 그들에게 새 신발과 축구복을 주었다.

**24** 몇몇은 심지어 경기를 보러 왔다. 이것은 소년들의 기분을 더 좋게 만들었다.

**25** 처음에, 사람들은 그들을 가장 약한 팀으로 보았다.

**26** 그러나 토너먼트가 시작되었을 때, 그 축구팀은 모든 사람들을 놀라게 했다.

**27** 준결승전 날, 비가 심하게 오고 있었다.

**28** 그들은 두 골 차로 지고 있었고, 이기는 것은 불가능해 보였다.

**29** "다른 팀이 아주 강해."라고 그들은 생각했다.

**30** 그러나 소년들은 포기하지 않았다.

**31** 그들은 후반전에 그들의 신발을 벗었고 경기는 완전히 바뀌었다.

**32** 고향의 미끄러운 축구장 덕분에 그들은 빗속에서 더 잘하였다.

**33** 비록 그들은 3대 2로 졌지만, 그들은 그들 자신이 자랑스러웠다.

**34** 그들은 그들이 지고 있을 때 포기하지 않았다. 그들은 끝까지 최선을 다하였다.

※ 다음 우리말을 영어로 쓰시오.

**1** Koh Panyee는 바다 가운데 떠 있는 작은 수상 마을이었다.

➡ _____

**2** 비록 그 마을의 소년들은 이전에 축구를 해 본 적이 없었지만, 그들은 그것을 TV로 보는 것을 정말 좋아했다.

➡ _____

**3** 어느 날, 그 소년들은 그들만의 축구팀을 만들기로 하였다.

➡ _____

**4** 그러나 사람들은 그들의 생각을 비웃었다.

➡ _____

**5** "그것은 불가능해."

➡ _____

**6** "왜 그렇게 말하는 거죠?"

➡ _____

**7** "주위를 둘러봐. 너희는 어디서 축구를 할 거니?"

➡ _____

**8** 마을 사람들이 옳았다. 소년들은 축구를 할 장소가 없었다.

➡ _____

**9** 그들은 낙담했다.

➡ _____

**10** "포기하지 마! 우리는 여전히 축구를 할 수 있어."

➡ _____

**11** "어떻게?"

➡ _____

**12** "우리만의 축구장을 만들자."

➡ _____

**13** 소년들은 낡은 배와 나뭇조각들을 모았다.

➡ _____

**14** 그들은 배를 합치고 그것들 위에 나무를 못으로 박았다.

➡ _____

**15** 매우 열심히 일한 후, 그들은 마침내 떠 있는 축구장을 가지게 되었다.

➡ _____

**16** 그것은 흔들리고 곳곳에 못이 있었다.

➡ _____

**17** 공과 소년들은 종종 바다에 빠졌고, 축구장은 항상 젖어 있고 미끄러웠다.

➡ _____

**18** 그들은 신발이 없어서 맨발로 축구를 해야 했다.

➡ _____

**19** 그런데도 그들은 상관하지 않았다.

➡ _____

**20** 실제로 그들은 훌륭한 기술을 쌓았고 더욱 더 축구를 즐겼다.

➡ _____

**21** 어느 날, 한 소년이 축구 토너먼트에 관한 포스터를 가지고 왔다.

➡ _____

**22** 그들은 한번 해 보기로 결정했다.

➡ _____

**23** 그들이 떠나려고 할 때, 마을 사람들은 그들에게 새 신발과 축구복을 주었다.

➡ _____

**24** 몇몇은 심지어 경기를 보러 왔다. 이것은 소년들의 기분을 더 좋게 만들었다.

➡ _____

**25** 처음에, 사람들은 그들을 가장 약한 팀으로 보았다.

➡ _____

**26** 그러나 토너먼트가 시작되었을 때, 그 축구팀은 모든 사람들을 놀라게 했다.

➡ _____

**27** 준결승전 날, 비가 심하게 오고 있었다.

➡ _____

**28** 그들은 두 골 차로 지고 있었고, 이기는 것은 불가능해 보였다.

➡ _____

**29** "다른 팀이 아주 강해."라고 그들은 생각했다.

➡ _____

**30** 그러나 소년들은 포기하지 않았다.

➡ _____

**31** 그들은 후반전에 그들의 신발을 벗었고 경기는 완전히 바뀌었다.

➡ _____

**32** 고향의 미끄러운 축구장 덕분에 그들은 빗속에서 더 잘하였다.

➡ _____

**33** 비록 그들은 3대 2로 졌지만, 그들은 그들 자신이 자랑스러웠다.

➡ _____

**34** 그들은 그들이 지고 있을 때 포기하지 않았다. 그들은 끝까지 최선을 다하였다.

➡ _____

※ 다음 우리말과 일치하도록 빈칸에 알맞은 말을 쓰시오.

**Real Life Communication - Step 2**

1. A: I _____ _____ _____ a basketball player _____ I'm
   _____ _____. Should I _____ _____?
2. B: No, _____ _____ _____! _____ you _____ _____
   of Anthony Webb?
3. A: No, I _____. Who is he?
4. B: He was a _____ _____. He was _____, but he _____
   the 1986 Slam Dunk Contest.

1. A: 나는 농구 선수가 되고 싶어. 근데 나는 키가 너무 작아. 내가 포기해야 할까?
2. B: 아니, 포기하지 마! Anthony Webb 에 대해 들어 봤니?
3. A: 아니, 그가 누군데?
4. B: 그는 농구선수였어. 그는 키가 작았지만, 1986 Slam Dunk Contest에서 우승했어.

**Culture & Life**

1. The women's field hockey team _____ Zimbabwe _____ the
   _____ _____.
2. _____ they had _____ _____ _____ _____,
   they _____ the gold medal _____ the 1980 Olympic Games.

1. 짐바브웨 여자 필드하키 팀은 전 세계를 놀라게 했다.
2. 비록 그들은 준비할 시간이 한 달밖에 없었지만, 그들은 1980년 올림픽 게임에서 금메달을 땄다.

**Let's Write**

1. _____ _____ _____ is basketball.
2. _____, I _____ really _____ _____ it at first.
3. I couldn't shoot well _____ _____ _____.
4. Although I _____ _____, I didn't _____ _____.
5. I _____ shooting _____ _____ _____ _____ _____.
6. This _____ _____ _____ well. Now, I'm _____ _____
   _____ on our team.

1. 내가 가장 좋아하는 운동은 농구이다.
2. 그러나 처음에 나는 농구를 잘하지 못했다.
3. 나는 다른 선수들과 달리 슛을 잘하지 못했다.
4. 나는 낙담했지만, 포기하지 않았다.
5. 나는 매일 한 시간 동안 슛 연습을 했다.
6. 이것이 내가 슛을 잘하게 했다. 이제, 나는 우리 팀에서 가장 잘하는 선수이다.

※ 다음 우리말을 영어로 쓰시오.

## Real Life Communication - Step 2

1. A: 나는 농구 선수가 되고 싶어. 근데 나는 키가 너무 작아. 내가 포기해야 할까?

   ➡ _____

2. B: 아니, 포기하지 마! Anthony Webb에 대해 들어 봤니?

   ➡ _____

3. A: 아니, 그가 누군데?

   ➡ _____

4. B: 그는 농구선수였어. 그는 키가 작았지만, 1986 Slam Dunk Contest에서 우승했어.

   ➡ _____

## Culture & Life

1. 짐바브웨 여자 필드하키 팀은 전 세계를 놀라게 했다.

   ➡ _____

2. 비록 그들은 준비할 시간이 한 달밖에 없었지만, 그들은 1980년 올림픽 게임에서 금메달을 땄다.

   ➡ _____

## Let's Write

1. 내가 가장 좋아하는 운동은 농구이다.

   ➡ _____

2. 그러나 처음에 나는 농구를 잘하지 못했다.

   ➡ _____

3. 나는 다른 선수들과 달리 슛을 잘하지 못했다.

   ➡ _____

4. 나는 낙담했지만, 포기하지 않았다.

   ➡ _____

5. 나는 매일 한 시간 동안 슛 연습을 했다.

   ➡ _____

6. 이것이 내가 슛을 잘하게 했다. 이제, 나는 우리 팀에서 가장 잘하는 선수이다.

   ➡ _____

# MEMO

영어 기출 문제집

적중100

2학기

# 정답 및 해설

지학 | 민찬규

중 2

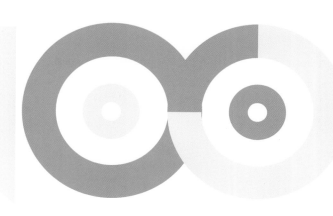

# Magic or Science?

## Conversation

p.10~11

**1** (1) Which country (2) Which sport
(3) Which one is stronger

**2** (1) can't wait (2) looking forward to meeting
(3) can't wait to see you again

---

### 시험대비 실력평가
p.08

01 disappear 　　02 ① 　　03 ④

04 ② 　　05 ① 　　06 (1) trick (2) material (3)
prepares (4) necessary (5) pressure (6) expand

01 주어진 관계는 반의어 관계를 나타낸다. disappear: 사라지다
02 '크기, 범위, 또는 양에서 증가하다'를 가리키는 말은 expand(팽창하다)이다.
03 confuse: 혼동하다
04 necessary: 필요한
05 주어진 문장에서 rose는 rise(오르다, 올라가다)의 과거형으로 이와 같은 의미를 가진 것은 ①번이다. 나머지는 모두 '장미'를 뜻한다.
06 trick: 마술, 속임수, material: 재료, 물질, prepare: 준비하다, necessary: 필요한, pressure: 압력, expand: 팽창하다, 확장하다

### 교과서 대화문 익히기

### Check(√) True or False
p.12

1 T　　2 F　　3 T　　4 T

---

### 서술형 시험대비
p.09

01 float
02 (1) see through (2) turn, into (3) burned out
(4) cooled down (5) stick to
03 (1) instead (2) float (3) magic (4) pushed
04 (1) It is not good to pick out vegetables that you
don't like.
(2) I'll give it a try.
(3) If you are sleepy, drink a glass of cold water.
(4) I signed up for the badminton class.
05 (1) sunburn (2) Hold (3) expands
(4) coin (5) escape (6) contract

01 주어진 관계는 반의어 관계를 나타낸다. sink: 가라앉다, float: 뜨다
02 tick to: ~을 고수하다, cool down: 차가워지다, see through: 속을 들여다보다, turn A into B: A를 B로 바꾸다, burn out: 타 버리다
03 instead of: ~ 대신에, float: 뜨다, magic: 마술의, push: 밀다
04 pick out 골라내다, give it a try 시도해 보다, a glass of 한 잔의, sign up for ~을 신청하다
05 hold: 잡다, coin: 동전, sunburn: 볕에 탐, expand: 팽창하다, escape: 탈출하다, 새다 contract: 수축하다

### 교과서 확인학습
p.14~15

**Listen & Speak 1 A**
Which flavor, First, half a cup, Next, mix, freezer, try making

**Listen & Speak 1 B**
put / picking out / Which, which / that sink in water, float / interesting, float / inside, like, balloon

**Listen & Speak 2 A**
a glass of, weigh / test / instead of / weigh, put / compare / can't wait to

**Listen & Speak 2 B**
hasn't rained / lasting, worried / should / clock / seasons, to prepare for, dry season / like / give it a try / can't wait to see your clock

**Real Life Communication A**
join / signed up for, fall / wait to, tricks / cool, Have you learned / practice / some day

**Let's Check**
magic, science / interesting / introduces, use science / half / cool, some / balloon / wait to

### 시험대비 기본평가
p.16

01 ⓔ → see 　　02 ⑤
03 Which class did you sign up for? 　　04 ①

01 I can't wait to 동사원형: 나는 ~이 무척 기다려져.
04 Mina는 새로운 마술 묘기를 배우게 돼서 신이 나 있다.

## 시험대비 실력평가 p.17~18

01 isn't it?　02 Sugar　03 ⑤　04 ③
05 물 위에 뜨는 달걀　06 ③　07 ④
08 ⑤　09 ②　10 ⑤

01 부가의문문으로 앞의 문장의 주어가 it이며 긍정문이므로 'isn't it?'이 적절하다.
02 설탕은 반 컵이 필요하다.
03 집에서 아이스크림을 만들어 볼 것을 제안한다.
04 (A)는 둘 중에서 선택하는 것이므로 which, (B)는 주어가 Eggs이므로 동사는 are, (C)는 주어와 동사가 있는 절이 이어지므로 because가 적절하다.
06 상한 달걀 속에 가스가 찬다.
07 주어진 문장은 시계가 어떻게 도움이 되는지에 대한 대답이므로 (D)가 적절하다.
08 세종대왕이 걷기를 끝내기 위해 무엇을 하는지 알 수 없다.
09 마술 수업에 등록한 상대방에게 '멋지다'라고 호응해 주는 표현이 적절하다.
10 얼마나 오랫동안 미나가 마술 묘기를 연습해 왔는지는 알 수 없다.

## 서술형 시험대비 p.19

01 I can't wait to see the difference.
02 She will use a finger.
03 a glass of water weighs more when there's a fish in it
04 (D) → (B) → (E) → (C) → (A)
05 We need to prepare two cups of milk, two cups of heavy cream, half a cup of sugar, and five strawberries.
06 We should mix everything together and put it in the freezer.

02 정 선생님은 물고기 대신 손가락을 사용할 것이다.
03 정 선생님은 재민이와 실험을 통해 물 한 잔이 물속에 물고기가 있을 때 무게가 더 나가는지 아닌지 확인하고 싶어 한다.
04 (D) 시계를 만들 것을 제안 → (B) 어떻게 도움이 될지 질문 → (E) 도움이 되는 이유 설명 → (C) 관심 표현 및 질문 → (A) 대답 및 이유 설명
05 Jane에 따르면 딸기 아이스크림을 만들기 위해 두 컵의 우유, 두 컵의 헤비 크림, 반 컵의 설탕, 그리고 5개의 딸기를 준비해야 한다.

06 딸기를 작게 자른 다음 모든 것을 섞어서 냉동실에 넣어야 한다.

## 교과서 Grammar

### 핵심 Check p.20~21

1 (1) to take care　(2) to meet　(3) for us to stay
2 (1) How come　(2) Why　(3) How come　(4) How come

## 시험대비 기본평가 p.22

01 (1) stop → to stop
　(2) of you → for you
　(3) did you meet → you meet
　(4) came → come
02 (1) he drinks (2) do you exercise
　(3) she looks (4) did you run
03 (1) It is very important to exercise regularly.
　(2) It is exciting to go to the amusement park.
　(3) It is important to be honest with your friends.
　(4) It is my job to explain it.

01 (1) 진주어로 쓰이는 것은 to부정사이다. (2) 상황에 대한 의견을 나타내는 형용사가 나오므로 의미상 주어로 'for+목적격'을 쓴다. (3) How come을 Why로 바꾸어도 좋다. (4) '도대체 왜 …?' 라고 쓰이는 것은 'How come'이다.
02 'How come+주어+동사 …?'로 쓰여 '도대체 왜 …?'라는 의미이고, 'Why+동사+주어 …?' 어 순임에 유의한다.
03 가주어 it을 대신하여 진주어 to부정사를 사용하여 문장을 쓸 수 있다.

## 시험대비 실력평가 p.23~25

01 ②　02 ③　03 ④　04 It is fun to learn a foreign language.　05 ②　06 ④
07 ⑤　08 to read books　09 ④
10 ③　11 ③　12 ③　13 How come she bought the jacket?　14 ⑤
15 ④　16 It is important not to use your phone while walking.　17 she left　18 ③
19 ③, ④　20 ③　21 It is dangerous to tell a stranger where you live.　22 ③　23 ⑤
24 How come you called me?

3

01 진주어이므로 to부정사를 쓰는 것이 적절하다.

02 'How come+주어+동사' 어순에 유의한다.

03 easy는 사람의 성질을 나타내는 형용사가 아니므로 의미상의 주어로 'for+목적격'을 쓴다. 나머지는 모두 of를 사용한다.

04 '외국어를 배우는 것'이 주어이므로 to learn a foreign language라고 쓴다.

05 주어진 문장의 밑줄 친 부분은 진주어로 쓰인 to부정사이다. ①, ④ 부사적 용법 중 목적 ② 진주어 ③ 형용사적 용법 ⑤ 명사적 용법(목적격 보어)

06 진주어로 쓰일 수 있는 것은 to부정사이며, 의문문에서 '주어+동사' 어순을 이끄는 것은 How come이다.

07 '주어+동사'의 어순을 이끄는 것은 'How come'이고, '동사+주어'의 어순을 이끄는 것은 'Why'이다.

08 진주어로 to부정사를 쓰는 것이 적절하다.

09 It is nice to know how to say hello.

10 모두 가주어 It이지만, ③번의 It은 날짜, 날씨, 거리, 명암 등을 나타내는 비인칭 주어이다.

11 진주어로 쓰일 수 있는 것은 It이다.

12 careless는 '부주의한'이란 의미로 사람의 성격을 나타내는 형용사이므로 의미상의 주어로 'of+목적격'을 써야 한다.

13 'How come+주어+동사' 어순에 유의한다.

14 impossible은 사람의 성격과 관련된 형용사가 아니므로 의미상의 주어로 'for+목적격'을 쓴다.

15 '주어+동사' 어순의 의문문이므로 How come이 적절하다.

16 휴대 전화기를 사용하지 않는 것이라고 하였으므로 to부정사의 부정으로 'not to V'를 쓰는 것에 유의한다.

17 How come이 이끄는 문장의 어순은 '주어+동사'임에 유의한다.

18 wise는 사람의 성격을 나타내는 형용사이므로 의미상의 주어로 'of+목적격'을 쓴다. 절이 이어지고 있으므로 두 번째 빈칸에는 진주어절을 이끄는 that을 쓴다.

19 '부주의하게 운전하는 것'이 주어이므로 주어를 to drive carelessly라고 쓰는 것이 적절하다.

20 모두 가주어 it에 진주어 to부정사가 쓰이지만, ③번에는 전치사 at의 목적어로 동명사 building이 쓰인다.

21 가주어 it을 이용하여 진주어 구문을 문장 맨 뒤로 보내어 같은 의미의 문장을 쓸 수 있다.

22 어순으로 보아 How come이 적절하며, impossible은 사람의 성격을 나타내는 형용사가 아니므로 의미상의 주어 로 'for+목적격'을 쓰는 것이 적절하다.

23 ① hear → to hear ② did you lose → you lost ③ for you → of you ④ you weren't → weren't you

24 How come은 'How come+주어+동사 ~?' 어순임에 유의한다.

---

01 It is dangerous not to wear your helmet.

02 (1) she is looking (2) did you invite
(3) the teacher gives (4) we are going
(5) are you wearing

03 (1) is exciting to travel abroad
(2) is not easy to read this novel
(3) know how to use this machine is useful

04 It was stupid of you to say so.

05 How come you put your wallet on the table?

06 for me to climb

07 How come you are going to meet her today?

08 that

09 How come / Why

10 to form good habits

11 A: How come she doesn't say sorry to me?
B: I think (that) it is not easy for her to say sorry to you.

12 of

13 How come you forgot to bring the book?

14 It was generous of him to lend you his clothes.

15 How come you booked the restaurant?

16 To watch the movie

17 How come / Why didn't you

18 A: How come you study hard?
B: It makes me happy to study hard.

---

01 '헬멧을 쓰지 않는 것'이 주어이므로 to부정사 진주어 앞에 부정어 not을 쓰는 것에 유의한다.

02 의문사 why와 how come은 의미는 비슷하지만 어순상의 차이를 보인다. 'How come+주어+동사 …'로 쓰여 '도대체 왜 …?'라는 의미이지만, 'Why+동사+주어 …?' 어순으로 쓰인다.

03 to부정사구가 주어로 올 경우 주어가 길어지므로 가주어 it을 쓰고 to부정사구는 진주어로 만들어 문장 뒤로 보낸다.

04 '그렇게 말한 것'의 주체가 '너'이며, 사람의 성격을 나타내는 형용사가 쓰이고 있으므로 의미상의 주어로 'of you'를 쓰는 것이 적절하다.

05 'How come+주어+동사' 어순에 유의하여 답을 쓴다.

06 '산을 오르는 것'이 진주어이고 주체는 '나'이므로 for me to climb이라고 쓰는 것이 적절하다.

07 이어지는 답변에서 내가 그녀를 오늘 만나려는 이유를 설명하고 있으므로 '왜 오늘 그녀를 만나려고 하는 거야?'라고 질문했음을 알 수 있다.

08 절을 이끌고 있으므로 진주어 절을 이끄는 that이 오는 것이 적절하다.

09 비슷한 의미를 가졌지만 How come은 '주어+동사' 어순을 이끌고 Why는 '동사+주어' 어순을 이끈다.

10 이어지는 답변으로 보아 '좋은 습관을 형성하는 것은 쉬운가요?'라고 질문했음을 알 수 있다.

11 '너에게 미안하다고 말하는 것'의 주체가 '그녀'이며 easy는 사람의 성격을 나타내는 형용사가 아니므로 의미상의 주어 로 'for her'를 쓰는 것에 유의한다.

12 사람의 성격과 관련된 형용사가 나와 있으므로 의미상의 주어로 'of+목적격'을 쓴다.

13 'How come+주어+동사' 어순임에 유의한다.

14 generous는 사람의 성격을 나타내는 형용사이므로 의미상의 주어로 'of+목적격'을 쓰는 것에 유의한다.

15 How come은 '주어+동사' 어순을 이끈다.

16 '그 영화를 보는 것'이라는 주어를 쓰는 것이 적절하다.

17 'How come+주어+동사'로 쓰이고 'Why+동사+ 주어' 어순임에 유의한다.

18 A: 'How come+주어+동사' 어순이며, '공부를 열심히 하는 것'이 주어이므로 to study hard를 진주어로, it을 가주어로 써서 문장을 완성할 수 있다.

## Reading

**확인문제**                                         p.28

1 T   2 F   3 F   4 F   5 T

**확인문제**                                         p.29

1 T   2 T   3 T   4 F   5 T   6 T

### 교과서 확인학습 A                               p.30~31

01 Welcome to   02 It's, exciting to see

03 to find out, behind   04 is science

05 will use science to perform

06 will, show us, to see them

07 to show you   08 with water in it

09 put a candle   10 light, cover it with

11 at, How come, rose into

12 expands, hot, higher pressure

13 gets cold, contracts, lower pressure

14 burnt out, lower pressure

15 cooled down, dropped

16 was at a higher pressure   17 pushed, into

18 to fill one of these cups

19 them around to confuse   20 which cup

21 It's, one   22 let's check

23 me the other cups   24 no water

25 How come, disappeared

26 Before, put, into, the cups

27 absorbed, turned it into

28 stuck to the bottom

29 necessary to us, that

30 for, performance, amazing

### 교과서 확인학습 B                               p.32~33

1 Jina: Welcome to the Super Science Magic Show!

2 It's always exciting to see magic tricks.

3 And it's more exciting to find out the secrets behind them.

4 Some people think the secret of magic is science.

5 Today, Ken, a member of the School Magic Club, will use science to perform his tricks.

6 Which tricks will he show us? I can't wait to see them.

7 Ken: Hello, everyone. Today, I'm going to show you something amazing.

8 Here's a dish with water in it.

9 Now, I'll put a candle in the middle of the dish.

10 Next, I'll light the candle and cover it with a glass. "Abracadabra!"

11 Jina: Look at the water! How come it rose into the glass?

12 Ken: Air expands when it gets hot and creates higher pressure.

13 When it gets cold, air contracts and creates lower pressure.

14 When the flame burnt out, the air inside the glass cooled down.

15 As the air cooled down, the air pressure dropped.

16 So the air outside the glass was at a higher pressure.

17 It pushed the water into the glass.

18 Ken: Now, I'm going to fill one of these cups with water.

19 I will move them around to confuse you.

20 Jina, which cup has the water in it?

21 Jina: That's easy! It's the middle one.

22 Ken: Okay, let's check. See? No water.

23 Jina: Show me the other cups.

24 Ken: See? There's no water.

25 Jina: Wow! How come the water disappeared?

26 Ken: Before the trick, I put a special material into one of the cups.

27 The material absorbed the water and turned it into jelly.

28 Then the jelly stuck to the bottom.

29 If you want to try this trick, it's necessary to use cups that you can't see through.

30 Jina: Thank you for your great performance. It was really amazing!

## 시험대비 실력평가
p.34~.37

01 ② 02 ③ 03 Ken is a member of the School Magic Club. 04 ③ 05 ② 06 ④ 07 The water outside the glass rose into the glass. 08 ② 09 change 10 ④ 11 ③ 12 absorb 13 He moved them around. 14 It is necessary for us to use cups that we can't see through. 15 ④ 16 ③ 17 magic tricks 18 ④ 19 ⑤ 20 ④ 21 The air inside the glass is at a higher pressure. 22 ① 23 The Amazing Rising Water disappeared? 25 ③ 26 ⑤ 27 He moved them around to confuse us. 28 ④ 24 How come the water 29 ice and wind

01 Welcome to ~.: ~에 오신 것을 환영합니다.

02 과학을 이용한 마술에 관한 이야기를 하려고 한다.

03 Kevin은 학교 마술 동아리 회원이라고 하였다.

04 공기가 뜨거워질 때 팽창한다면, 반대로 공기가 차가워질 경우 수축하면서 더 낮은 압력을 만드는 것을 유추할 수 있다.

05 불꽃이 다 타버리면 컵 속의 공기는 식어버리므로 'cooled down'이 적절하다.

06 Ken은 물이 든 접시 위의 초를 유리컵으로 덮었다고 하였다. 따라서 ④번은 찾아볼 수 없다.

07 Ken이 유리컵으로 초를 덮을 때, 유리컵 밖에 있던 물이 유리컵 속으로 올라갔다.

08 Ken은 놀라운 어떤 것을 보여주기를 원하였고, 이는 과학을 적용한 마술이다.

09 글의 내용으로 보아 유리컵의 내부와 외부의 압력 변화로 인하여 물이 움직이게 되는 것을 알 수 있다. difference라고 써도 좋다.

10 이어지는 대화 내용으로 보아 나머지 모든 컵을 보여 달라고 했음을 유추할 수 있다.

11 the jelly는 물을 흡수한 특별한 물질이 변화하여 만들어진 것이다. 따라서 ③번이 가장 적절하다.

12 자연스럽거나 점진적인 방식으로 무언가를 받아들이는 것은 '흡수하다(absorb)'이다.

13 Ken은 컵들 중 하나에 물을 채운 후 컵들을 섞었다.

14 마술을 해 보고자 한다면, 속을 들여다볼 수 없는 컵을 사용해야 한다고 하였다.

15 Ken의 마술은 과학을 이용한 것이며 투명한 유리컵이 아니라 불투명한 컵을 이용해야 한다.

16 밑줄 친 (A)는 가주어 It이다. ①, ④ 비인칭 주어 ②, ⑤ 인칭 대명사 ③ 가주어

17 마술을 가리키는 대명사이다.

18 마술 동아리 회원인 Ken은 마술을 수행하기 위해 과학을 사용할 것이라고 하며 그를 소개하고 있으므로 ④번이 가장 적절하다.

19 이어지는 Ken의 설명으로 보아 왜 물이 유리컵 속으로 올라간 것인지를 묻는 말이 적절하다.

20 (C)에서 물이 담긴 접시가 처음으로 등장하고 (B) 그 접시 한가운데에 초를 놓고 (A) 그 초를 켜는 순서가 적절하다.

21 초가 타는 동안은 뜨거운 공기의 팽창으로 인하여 높은 압력이 만들어지므로 유리컵 내부의 공기가 더 높은 압력을 가진다.

22 '-thing, -body, -one'으로 끝나는 부정대명사는 형용사의 수식을 뒤에서 받는다. 따라서 something amazing 이라고 쓰는 것이 적절하다.

23 '신비한 솟아오르는 물'이 적절하다.

24 How come은 '주어+동사' 어순을 이끄는 것에 유의한다.

25 물을 흡수하면 그것을 젤리로 변하게 한다고 하였다.

26 (C)는 관계대명사 that으로 불완전한 문장을 이끈다. 모두 완전한 문장을 이끄는 명사절 접속사이지만 ⑤번은 관계대명사이다.

27 헷갈리게 하기 위해서 컵을 이리저리 섞는 것이라고 하였다.

28 on one's own: 혼자서, 혼자 힘으로

29 과학자들의 연구에 따르면 얼음과 바람이 바위가 혼자 움직이는 것처럼 보이게 만든다.

## 서술형 시험대비
p.38~39

01 It is more exciting to find out the secrets behind magic tricks.

02 He will perform his magic tricks.

03 to see magic tricks

04 How come

05 He put the candle in the middle of the dish.

06 It expands.

07 lower pressure

08 Rising, burnt out, cooled, dropped, higher, outside, pushed

09 which has the water in it

10 It sticks to the bottom of the cup.

11 it is necessary to use cups that you can't see through

12 your performance

13 We need to prepare a coin and a bottle.

14 it is important to cool the bottle

15 on the bottom → on the mouth / spin → move up and down

01 마술 뒤에 숨겨진 비밀에 관하여 알아내는 것이 더 신나는 일이라고 하였다.

02 Ken은 자신의 마술을 보여줄 것이라고 하였다.

03 가주어 It이므로 진주어를 의미하는 것이다.

04 이어지는 말에서 물이 솟아오르는 원리를 설명하고 있다.

05 Ken은 접시 한가운데에 초를 놓았다.

06 공기가 뜨거워지면 팽창한다고 하였다.

07 공기가 차가워지면 수축하면서 낮은 압력을 만들어 낸다고 하였다.

08 솟아오르는 물 마술이다. 불꽃이 다 타 버렸을 때 유리컵 안의 공기는 차가워지고 압력은 떨어졌다. 유리컵 밖의 높은 압력이 물을 유리컵 안으로 밀어 올렸다.

09 지나는 물이 있는 컵이 가운데 컵이라고 생각하였다.

10 젤리로 변한 물은 컵 바닥에 달라붙는다고 하였다.

11 가주어 it을 활용하여 같은 의미의 문장을 쓸 수 있다.

12 Ken이 한 공연을 가리키는 말이다.

13 마술을 하기 위해서는 동전과 병이 필요하다고 하였다.

14 가주어 it을 활용하여 문장을 쓸 수 있다. '병을 차갑게 하는 것'이 주어이므로 to cool the bottle을 주어로 문장을 만든다.

15 동전을 병 입구에 올려놓는 것이고, 손으로 잠시 병을 쥐고 있으면 동전이 위아래로 움직인다고 하였다. spin: 돌다

## 영역별 핵심문제

p.41~45

01 ②　　　　02 ⑤

03 (1) turn into　(2) cooled down
　　(3) see through　(4) turned, into

04 ②　　　　05 ②

06 (1) Which flame will burn out first?
　　(2) My daughter blew out the candles on her cake.
　　(3) Water expands and contracts with changes in temperature.

07 ③　　　　08 ⓓ → sounds　　　　09 ②

10 ⑤　　　　11 sink　　　　12 ⑤

13 (A) flavor　(B) strawberry　(C) mix
　　(D) cut　(E) put　(F) try

14 ④　　　　15 ②　　　　16 ④　　　　17 ③

18 It is not easy for her to move the boxes.

19 ③　　　　20 ④　　　　21 ⑤　　　　22 ③

23 How come she made an appointment?

24 for him　　25 ⑤　　　　26 ④

27 ⓓ-ⓒ-ⓐ-ⓑ

28 the air outside the glass　29 ⑤　　　30 expand

31 ②　　　　　　32 ⑤

01 '불가능한 일들이 일어나게 만드는 힘을 가진' 것을 가리키는 것은 magic(마법의, 마술의)이다.

02 sink: 가라앉다

03 turn A into B A를 B로 바꾸다, cool down 차가워지다, see through 속을 들여다 보다

04 주어진 문장에서 sink(싱크대)를 가리킨다. ②번의 sink는 '가라앉다'를 가리킨다.

05 mix: 섞다; 혼합물, flour: 밀가루

06 flame: 불꽃, candle: 양초, expand: 팽창하다, contract: 수축하다

07 어느 계란들이 신선한지 묻는 질문에 차이를 구별하고 싶다는 대답은 어색하다.

08 주어가 3인칭 That이므로 단수 동사 sounds가 적절하다.

09 세종대왕은 비가 오랫동안 내리지 않아 걱정했지만 장영실이 시계를 만들어 건기를 대비하기 위해 사용할 수 있도록 한다는 이야기를 듣고 기뻐함을 알 수 있다.

11 '물의 표면 아래로 내려가다'를 가리키는 말은 sink(가라앉다)이다.

12 유진이가 풍선을 갖고 무엇을 하려고 하는지는 알 수 없다.

13 strawberry: 딸기, put A in B: A를 B에 놓다, mix: 섞다, cut: 자르다, flavor: 맛

14 '우리를 위해 나서 준 것'이 주어이며 이것의 주체가 '너'이고 사람의 성격을 나타내는 brave가 있으므로 의미상의 주어로 of you를 쓰는 것이 적절하다.

15 wise는 사람의 성격을 나타내는 형용사이므로 의미상의 주어로 'of+목적격'을 쓰는 것이 적절하다.

16 possible은 사람의 성격을 나타내는 형용사가 아니므로 의미상의 주어로 'for+목적격'을 쓴다.

17 모두 주어로 쓰인 to부정사이지만, ③번은 부사적 용법 중 '목적'으로 쓰여 '~하기 위해서'라고 해석된다. lay: (알을) 낳다

18 '그 상자들을 옮기는 것'이 주어이며 행위의 주체는 '그녀'이므로 'for her to move the boxes'라고 쓴다.

19 절을 이끌고 있으므로 두 번째 빈칸에는 that이 들어가야 하며, 첫 번째 빈칸에는 가주어 It이 적절하다.

20 모두 '주어+동사' 어순이므로 How come이 사용되지만 ④번은 '동사+주어' 어순이므로 Why가 쓰인다.

21 '주어+동사' 어순이므로 How come을 쓴다.

22 ① That → It ② for her → of her ④ play → to play ⑤ did he drink → he drank

23 How come은 '주어+동사' 어순을 이끄는 것에 유의한다.

24 strange는 의미상의 주어로 'for+목적격'을 쓴다.

25 (A)는 '불을 붙이다'는 의미로 쓰인 light이다. ① 빛 ② 전등,

7

(전깃)불 ③ (색깔이) 연한, 옅은 ④ 가벼운 ⑤ 불을 붙이다

**26** Jina가 왜 물이 유리컵 속으로 올라간 것인지를 묻고 있으므로 이에 대한 답변이 이어진다고 보는 것이 적절하다.

**27** ⓓ 초가 다 탔을 때 유리컵 내부의 공기가 식었음 ⓒ 공기가 식으면서 공기 압력이 떨어짐 ⓐ 그래서 유리컵 밖의 공기 압력이 더 높아짐 ⓑ 압력이 높아진 바깥 공기가 물을 밀어서 유리컵 안으로 들어가게 함

**28** 유리컵 밖의 공기를 가리키는 말이다.

**29** 유리컵 밖의 공기 압력이 더 높아지면서 높아진 압력의 공기가 물을 밀어서 유리컵 안으로 들어가는 것이 적절하다. 따라서 pushed라고 써야 한다. pull: 당기다

**30** 크기, 범위, 혹은 양에 있어서의 증가는 '팽창하다 (expand)'이다.

**31** 이어지는 대화 내용으로 보아 컵에 물을 채운 것임을 알 수 있다.

**32** 사라지는 물의 비밀이 가장 적절하다.

### 단원별 예상문제 p.46~49

01 Which flavor do you want to make? 02 mix
03 ③ 04 sink, float, gas, air 05 ⓒ → use 06 ⑤ 07 She signed up for a magic class. 08 She is looking forward to learning new magic tricks. 09 ⑤ 10 I'm looking forward to seeing the differences. 11 ③
12 ④ 13 It was wise of you to 14 ⑤
15 ④ 16 It is surprising that he won the competition. 17 How come you are home so early?
18 ② 19 ③ 20 **특별한 물질을 숨기기 위해서** 21 ③ 22 ⓐ How do you do it? ⓑ What happens? ⓒ How come the coin moves? 23 expanding 24 ③ 25 trying to escape from the bottle

**02** '두 개 이상의 물질을 결합하여 하나의 물질이 되게 하다'는 mix(섞다)이다.

**03** 주어진 문장은 어느 달걀들이 신선한지, 신선하지 않은지에 대한 대답이므로 (C)가 적절하다.

**04** 달걀이 물에 가라앉을 때, 그것들은 신선하다. 반면에 물에 뜨는 달걀은 신선하지 않다. 상한 달걀은 속에 가스가 찬다. 그것은 풍선 속의 공기처럼 활동한다.

**05** that의 선행사는 100 magic tricks이므로 동사는 use가 적절하다.

**06** 얼마나 오랫동안 지원이가 풍선 마술을 연습했는지는 알 수 없다.

**07** 미나는 이번 겨울에 마술 수업에 등록했다.

**08** 미나는 새로운 마술 묘기를 배우는 것을 기대하고 있다.

**09** 주어진 문장은 How will that work?에 대한 대답으로 적절하므로 (E)에 들어가는 것이 적절하다.

**11** I can't wait to ~ = I'm looking forward to -ing: 나는 ~이 무척 기다려져

**11** How come은 '주어+동사' 어순임에 유의한다.

**12** 모두 의미상의 주어로 'for+목적격'을 쓰는 형용사이지만, careful은 사람의 성격에 관련한 형용사이므로 의미상의 주어로 'of+목적격'을 쓴다.

**13** wise는 사람의 성격에 관련된 형용사이므로 의미상의 주어로 'of+목적격'을 써서 문장을 완성한다.

**14** ① to finding → to find ② is she → she is ③ to not follow → not to follow ④ he is → is he

**15** (A) 가주어는 It이 쓰인다. (B) 절을 이끌고 있으므로 that을 쓴다. (C) '주어+동사' 어순이므로 How come을 쓴다.

**16** '그가 그 대회에서 우승했다'는 것을 진주어절로 만들어 문장을 완성한다.

**17** 'How come+주어+동사' 어순에 유의한다.

**18** (A)는 '~하기 위해서'라고 해석되는 to부정사의 부사적 용법이다. ① 명사적 용법 중 목적격 보어 ② 부사적 용법 중 목적 ③ 형용사적 용법 ④ 진주어 ⑤ 명사적 용법 중 목적어

**19** Ken은 Jina가 혼란을 느끼도록 하기 위하여 컵들을 섞었다.

**20** Ken은 마술의 비밀이 특별한 물질 때문이라고 밝혔다. 이를 숨기기 위해서는 속을 들여다볼 수 없는 컵을 사용해야 한다.

**21** Ken은 마술 전에 특별한 물질을 컵 하나에 넣었다고 하였으므로 ③번이 가장 적절하다.

**22** ⓐ 이어지는 문장이 방법을 설명하고 있으므로 어떻게 하는 것인지 묻는 말이 적절하며, ⓑ 동전이 위아래로 움직인다고 말하고 있으므로 무슨 일이 발생하는지 묻는 말이 들어가는 것이 적절하며, ⓒ 그 원리를 설명하고 있으므로 왜 움직이는지 묻는 말이 자연스럽다.

**23** 손이 병 안의 찬 공기를 데우면 공기가 따뜻해져서 팽창한다. 팽창하는 공기가 병에서 나가려고 하는 것이므로 'expanding'을 쓴다.

**24** 병을 차갑게 하는 것이 중요하다고 하였다.

**25** 병을 탈출하려는 공기 때문에 병 입구에 놓인 동전이 위아래로 움직이는 것이다.

### 서술형 실전문제 p.50~51

01 It hasn't rained for a long time.
02 He suggests making a special clock.
03 It's because the clock will show the time and the seasons, so they can use it to prepare for the dry season.
04 It is rude of him to take pictures of her without her permission.
05 for him to
06 How come you couldn't catch the bus?
07 It is important to keep
08 How come they are tired?

09 He put a special material into one of the cups.

10 Ken put a special material into the cup and it absorbed the water and turned it into jelly.

11 Why did the water disappear?

12 (A) warm (B) gets (C) expands (D) escape

13 ⓑ−ⓓ−ⓐ−ⓒ

01 오랫동안 비가 내리지 않았다.

02 장영실은 특별한 시계를 만들 것을 제안한다.

03 시계는 시간과 계절을 알려줘 건기를 준비하기 위해 사용할 수 있기 때문에 장영실은 시계가 농부들을 도와줄 것이라고 생각한다.

04 of와 to를 추가한다. rude는 사람의 성격을 나타내는 형용사이므로 의미상의 주어로 'of+목적격'을 쓴다.

05 that절에서 운동하는 주체가 'he'이므로 to부정사 구문으로 바꿀 때 의미상의 주어를 'for him'으로 쓸 수 있다.

06 답변에서 버스를 타지 못한 이유를 설명하고 있으므로 '왜 버스를 타지 못했니?'라는 질문을 쓰는 것이 적절하다.

07 진주어로 to부정사를, 가주어로 It을 써서 나타낼 수 있다.

08 'How come+주어+동사' 어순임에 유의한다.

09 Ken은 컵들 중 하나에 특별한 물질을 넣었다고 하였다.

10 컵 안에 있는 물이 젤리로 변한 이유는, Ken이 넣어둔 특별한 물질이 물을 흡수하여 그것을 젤리로 변하게 만들었기 때문이다.

11 'How come+주어+동사' 어순이고, 'Why+동사+주어' 어순임에 유의한다.

12 차가운 병 속의 공기를 따뜻하게 하기 위해서 손으로 병을 쥐는 것이고, 병 속의 공기가 따뜻해지면서 공기가 팽창한다. 이 팽창하는 공기가 병에서 나가려고 하는 것이다.

13 ⓑ 병을 차갑게 하고 ⓓ 병 입구에 동전 하나를 올려둔 후 ⓐ 병을 두 손으로 잡고 ⓒ 얼마간의 시간이 지나면 동전이 움직일 것이다.

## 창의사고력 서술형 문제
p.52

01 (A) the dry season

(B) a special clock

(C) the time and seasons

(D) to prepare for the dry season

(E) time and the seasons

|모범답안|

02 (1) It is easy to make many friends.

(2) It is important to love your pet.

(3) It is necessary to save your allowance.

(4) It is hard to think others first.

01 세종대왕은 건기가 너무 오래 지속되고 있었기 때문에 농부들을 걱정했다. 그가 농부들을 도울 방법을 찾을 때 장영실은 특별한 시계를 만들 것을 제안하였다. 세종대왕은 어떻게 그 시계가 농부들을 도와줄 수 있을지 궁금했다. 장영실은 시계가 시간과 계

절을 보여주므로 건기를 준비하는데 사용될 수 있다고 설명했다. 다행히도, 장영실은 시간과 계절에 대해 많이 알고 있어서 그는 이것을 발명하기 위해 노력했다.

## 단원별 모의고사
p.53~56

01 ③　　02 (1) balloon　(2) candle　(3) compare

03 (1) pressure　(2) flames　(3) absorbs　(4) material

(5) experiment　04 100 magic tricks　　05 ⑤

06 I can't wait to learn new magic tricks there.

07 ④　　08 ③　　09 ⓒ → put　10 ⑤

11 The eggs that[which] float in the water are not fresh.　　12 The gas inside the eggs makes them float in the water.　　13 ④　　14 ⑤

15 ⑤　　16 of him not to　　17 How come he isn't coming to the party?

18 (B)−(D)−(A)−(C)　　19 absorbed, stuck, the bottom　　20 He will use science to perform his tricks.　　21 ③　　22 ④　　23 The water rose into the glass.　　24 ⑤　　25 He covered the candle with a glass.

01 '음식을 얼리거나 언채로 유지되도록 하기 위한 장치 또는 공간'을 가리키는 것은 freezer(냉동고)이다.

02 balloon: 풍선, candle: 양초, compare: 비교하다

03 flame: 불꽃, material: 재료, 물질, absorb: 흡수하다, pressure: 압력, experiment: 실험, bleed: 피흘리다

07 미나는 전에 마술 묘기를 배운 적이 있다.

07 I can't wait to ~: 나는 ~이 무척 기다려져. = I'm looking forward to ~ing

09 mix와 병렬구조를 이루는 동사로 put이 적절하다.

10 Jane은 썩은 것을 얼마나 오래 냉동실에 두어야 하는지 알 수 없다.

11 물에 뜨는 달걀들은 신선하지 않다.

12 달걀 안에 있는 가스가 그 달걀들을 물 위에 뜨게 만든다.

13 '주어+동사' 어순이므로 How come, clever는 사람의 성격을 나타내는 형용사이므로 to부정사의 의미상 주어로 'of+목적격'을 쓴다.

14 possible은 사람의 성격을 나타내는 형용사가 아니므로 의미상의 주어로 for him을 쓰는 것이 적절하다.

15 모두 가주어 It으로 쓰였지만 ⑤번은 명암을 나타내는 비인칭 용법이다.

16 to부정사의 부정은 'not to V' 형태이며, mean은 사람의 성격을 나타내는 형용사이므로 'of him'을 쓰는 것에 유의한다.

17 'How come+주어+동사' 어순임에 유의한다.

18 (B) 마술 전에 미리 특별한 물질을 넣어 둠 − (D) 이 물질이 물을 흡수하고 물을 젤리로 만듦 − (A) 그 젤리는 컵 바닥에 들러

붙음 - (C) 그러므로 이 마술을 하기 위해서는 반드시 속이 들여다 보이지 않는 컵을 써야 함.

19 컵 안에 있는 특별한 물질이 물을 흡수하고 그것을 젤리로 변하게 했다. 그리고 그 젤리는 바닥에 달라붙었다.

20 Ken은 자신의 마술을 위해 과학을 이용할 것이라고 하였다.

21 'I can't wait to ~'는 '나는 ~이 무척 기다려진다.'라는 뜻으로 'I'm looking forward to -ing'로 바꾸어 쓸 수 있다.

22 'How come+주어+동사' 어순이므로 How come을 쓰는 것이 적절하다. 'Why+동사+주어' 어순임에 유의하자.

23 물은 유리컵 안으로 솟아올랐다.

24 초가 얼마나 탔는지는 위 글을 읽고 답할 수 없다.

25 Ken은 초에 불을 붙인 후 유리컵으로 초를 덮었다.

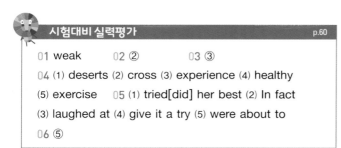

## Call It Courage

### 시험대비 실력평가      p.60

01 weak      02 ②      03 ③

04 (1) deserts (2) cross (3) experience (4) healthy

(5) exercise    05 (1) tried[did] her best (2) In fact

(3) laughed at (4) give it a try (5) were about to

06 ⑤

01 주어진 관계는 반의어 관계를 나타낸다.

02 '옷에 의해 덮여지지 않은'을 가리키는 말은 bare(벌거벗은)이다.

03 nail: 못질하다

04 exercise: 운동하다, desert: 사막, experience: 경험하다, cross: 건너다, healthy: 건강한

05 try[do] one's best: 최선을 다하다, in fact: 사실은, laugh at: 비웃다, give it a try: 시도해 보다, be about to: 막 ~하려고 하다

06 주어진 문장에서 cross는 '건너다'를 뜻한다. ⑤번은 '십자가'를 의미한다.

### 서술형 시험대비      p.61

01 discouraged

02 (1) took off (2) in front of (3) on foot (4) fall into

03 (1) match (2) against (3) weak (4) lose (5) meals

04 (1) I fell into a hole while walking along the road.

(2) You should try hard and never give up.

(3) Don't take off your coat.

05 (1) tried out for (2) give up (3) laughed at

(4) In fact (5) is good at

01 주어진 관계는 반의어 관계를 나타낸다. encouraged 용기를 북돋운, discouraged 낙담한

02 take off: 벗다, in front of: ~의 앞에, on foot: 걸어서, 도보로, fall into: ~에 빠지다

03 weak: 약한, meal: 식사, lose: 지다, match: 경기, against: ~에 맞서

04 fall into: ~에 빠지다, give up: 포기하다, take off: 벗다

05 laugh at: 비웃다, try out for: 지원하다, give up: 포기하다, be good at: ~을 잘하다, in fact: 사실 squad: 분대, 소집단, 일단(의 사람들), 한 조(組), 팀

### 교과서 Conversation

#### 핵심 Check      p.62~63

1 (1) Have you heard (2) Yes, I have

(3) No, I haven't

2 (1) Don't take it too hard

(2) Don't be so hard on yourself

(3) Cheer up, You can do it

### 교과서 대화문 익히기

#### Check(√) True or False      p.64

1 T   2 F   3 T   4 T

### 교과서 확인학습      p.66~67

**Listen & Speak 1 A**

have you heard / have / who crossed, on foot / took, about / experience, desert, cross / try, in

**Listen & Speak 1 B**

have you heard about / have, on / right / want to / I don't wear at home, if you want / in front of, go inside / See

**Listen & Speak 2 A**

healthy, exercise, try to, Don't eat, wash, meals, sound hard, take, step, give up, live, life

**Listen & Speak 2 B**

try out for, about / sure / Why not / trying out for / good at, don't give up / try my best

**Real Life Communication A**

excited, match / against, lose / Have you heard / No, haven't, about / so, lose / What happened / worked hard, won, give up / try our best

**Let's Check ❶**

Have you heard of, read well, lost, hearing in, Still, difficilties, be like, don't give up

### 시험대비 기본평가      p.68

01 Have you heard of Thomas Edison?     02 ②

03 ④      04 ⑤

**02** 밑줄 친 (B)는 '그럼에도, 그럼에도 불구하고'를 의미하며 이와 같은 의미를 나타내는 것은 ②번이다. 나머지는 모두 '여전히'를 의미한다.

**03** 주어진 문장의 이 조언들(these tips)을 (D) 앞에서 설명하고 있으므로 (D)가 적절하다.

---

시험대비 실력평가 p.69~70

01 desert  02 ③  03 ⑤  04 (E) → (B) → (D) → (A) → (C)  05 ⓔ → don't give up
06 첫째, 매일 운동할 것. 둘째, 건강에 좋은 음식을 먹을 것. 셋째, 식사 전에 손을 씻을 것.  07 ①  08 ⑤
09 ②  10 (A) ugly sweater (B) Sora's (C) she didn't wear

**01** '보통 모래로 덮여 있고 아주 더운 매우 건조한 땅의 지역'을 가리키는 말은 desert(사막)이다.

**02** (A) 알고 있는지 묻는 현재완료 시제의 질문에 대한 대답으로 'Yes, I have.'가 적절하다. (B) 선행사가 사람이므로 'who', (C) 내용의 흐름상 경험하고 싶지만 걸어서 사막을 건너고 싶지 않다는 역접의 접속사가 적절하므로 'but'이 적절하다.

**03** Tim은 고비 사막을 걸어서 건너고 싶지 않다고 이야기하였다.

**04** (E) 알고 있는지 질문 → (B) 모른다고 대답 → (D) 그리스 팀에 대한 설명 → (A) 구체적 설명 요청 → (C) 대답 및 격려하기

**05** 포기하지 말아야 건강한 삶을 살 것이라는 내용이 자연스러우므로 'don't give up'이 적절하다.

**07** 빈칸에 들어갈 말로 격려하는 표현이 적절하다.

**08** 호주이는 아이스하키 팀 지원에 최선을 다할 것이다.

**09** Alex는 "못생긴 스웨터 파티"에 가고 싶은데 스웨터가 없어서 우울했지만(depressed) 소라의 옷을 입고 갈 수 있게 되었으므로 기분이 좋아졌다(pleased).

**10** 비록 Alex는 그의 못생긴 스웨터가 없었지만 그는 소라의 도움으로 "못생긴 스웨터 파티"에 갈 수 있었다. 그는 그녀가 입지 않는 스웨터를 빌렸다. 그는 정말로 그녀에게 고마워했다.

---

서술형 시험대비 p.71

01 ⓓ → that 또는 which
02 December 5th / Student Center / an ugly sweater
03 (1) healthy (2) exercise (3) fast (4) wash (5) meals (6) tips (7) take
04 don't give up
05 ⓓ → Although[Though]
06 He couldn't read well and lost all of the hearing in his left ear.

---

**12** 정답 및 해설

---

**01** one이 가리키는 것은 an ugly sweater로 선행사가 사물이므로 that이나 which가 적절하다.

**05** Despite은 전치사이므로 접속사 Although[Though]가 적절하다.

**06** 그는 어렸을 때 글을 잘 읽지 못했고 왼쪽 귀가 전혀 들리지 않았다.

---

# Grammar

**핵심 Check** p.72~73

1 (1) us help  (2) him use  (3) done
2 (1) Although[Though]  (2) though[although]
  (3) Even though

---

시험대비 기본평가 p.74

01 (1) doing → do
   (2) thought → think
   (3) Despite → Although[Though]
   (4) Even → Even though
02 (1) had us sing (2) made me find
   (3) let me cook (4) had the project finished
03 (1) Although I like the house, it's too far from my school.
   (2) Though I was tired, I did my homework.
   (3) Julia studied although she was sleepy.
   (4) Though he is old, he is quite strong.

**01** (1) 사역동사의 목적격 보어는 동사원형의 형태이다. (2) 목적어와 목적격 보어의 관계가 수동일 경우 과거분사를 쓰며 his wife는 생각하는 주체가 되므로 think를 쓴다. (3) 절을 이끌고 있으므로 Although나 Though를 쓴다. Despite은 명사구를 이끈다. (4) Even은 형용사 혹은 부사로 쓰이므로 문장을 이끄는 Even though를 쓰는 것이 적절하다.

**02** 사역동사의 목적어와 목적격 보어의 관계가 능동인 경우, 목적격 보어로 동사원형을 쓴다. 단, 목적어와 목적격 보어의 관계가 수동인 경우 목적격 보어로 과거분사를 쓴다.

**03** (1), (2) 사역동사의 목적어와 목적격 보어의 관계가 능동인 경우 목적격 보어로 동사원형을 쓴다. (3), (4) '비록 ~일지라도'로 해석되며 문장을 이어주는 부사절 접속사는 though 혹은 although이다. 주절 앞에 쓰는 경우 콤마를 쓰는 것에 유의한다.

01 ③    02 ④    03 ⑤    04 I had my car fixed.   05 ①, ③    06 ③    07 ⑤

08 Although I like to swim in the river, I hate summer.

09 ⑤    10 ①    11 Although[Though] he wasn't hungry, he had dinner with her.   12 ⑤

13 ①    14 ③    15 planted    16 ④

17 ④    18 Please let me know what the answer is.   19 ③    20 ④    21 ④

22 They made me repeat the whole story.

23 Although    24 cut

01 사역동사 have의 목적어와 목적격 보어의 관계가 능동이므로 목적격 보어로 동사원형을 쓴다.

02 모두 인과 관계를 이끄는 Because가 쓰이지만 ④번에는 양보의 부사절 접속사 Although가 쓰인다.

03 despite은 명사구를 이끄는 전치사이다. 주어와 동사를 포함하는 절을 이끄는 것은 접속사이다.

04 차는 수리되는 것이므로 목적격 보어로 과거분사를 쓴다.

05 ② brought → bring ④ clean → cleaned ⑤ Despite → Although

06 사역동사로 쓰이면서 4, 5형식에 모두 쓰일 수 있는 동사는 make이다. get은 5형식에서 목적격 보어로 to부정사를 취한다.

07 주어진 문장의 밑줄 친 부분은 양보의 부사절을 이끄는 While로 쓰였다. While은 '~ 동안'이라는 의미도 가지고 있으며 ①~④번은 모두 그와 같은 의미이지만 ⑤번은 양보의 부사절을 이끄는 While로 쓰였다.

08 '비록 ~한다 할지라도'는 although 혹은 though 등으로 표현한다. to swim 대신에 swimming을 써도 좋다.

09 건물이 paint되는 것이므로 과거분사를 쓰는 것이 적절하다.

10 명사구를 이끌고 있으므로 접속사 Even though가 아닌 전치사 Despite을 쓰는 것이 적절하다.

11 비록 배가 고프지 않았지만, 그는 그녀와 함께 저녁을 먹었다는 의미로 쓰는 것이 적절하며 although절을 주절 뒤에 쓸 경우 콤마를 쓰지 않음에 유의한다.

12 목적격 보어로 동사원형이 쓰이고 있으므로 want는 빈칸에 적절하지 않다. want는 to부정사를 목적격 보어로 취하는 동사이다.

13 명사구를 이끌고 있으므로 전치사 despite 혹은 in spite of, 사역동사 have의 목적격 보어로 쓰이며 목적어와 능동 관계에 있으므로 동사원형 형태를 쓰는 것이 적절하다.

14 주어진 문장의 빈칸에는 양보의 부사절을 이끄는 접속사 although 등이 쓰인다. ① When ② After ③ Although ④ Because ⑤ If

15 나무는 심어지는 것이므로 과거분사를 쓴다.

16 '늦었음에도 불구하고, 그는 그 방으로 들어가는 것이 허락되었다'라는 의미이다. 따라서 ④번이 적절하다.

17 모두 동사원형을 목적격 보어로 취하는 동사이지만 allow는 to 부정사를 목적격 보어로 취한다.

18 사역동사 let은 목적어와 목적격 보어의 관계가 능동인 경우 목적격 보어로 동사원형을 쓴다.

19 make는 사역동사이며 목적어와 목적격 보어의 관계가 능동이므로 take가 적절하다.

20 Despite은 전치사이므로 문장을 이끌 수 없다.

21 사역동사의 목적어와 목적격 보어의 관계가 능동일 경우 목적격 보어로 동사원형을 쓰는 것이 적절하다.

22 이야기를 반복하는 주체가 '나'이며 그들이 나에게 시킨 것이므로 사역동사를 사용하되 목적격 보어로 동사원형을 쓰는 것이 적절하다.

23 Though, While, Even though를 써도 좋다.

24 사역동사 have의 목적어와 목적격 보어의 관계가 수동일 경우 목적격 보어로 과거분사를 쓴다.

01 Though I got up early, I was late for school.

02 (1) take care of my baby sister
   (2) water the flowers
   (3) brush my teeth after dinner

03 (1) cross (2) stolen (3) sliced

04 Although the man hurt his leg, he could walk.
Although it rained a lot, we went to the zoo.
Although Clara brought her umbrella, she was wet.

05 laugh

06 (1) although[even though] (2) Despite
   (3) Even though[Although]

07 had people shout, made our team feel strong, let the other team win

08 Even though it was windy, I went out to play soccer.

09 me exercise

10 Jenny let her dog run around.

11 (1) Although there was a heavy storm, people were safe inside.
   (2) Although his throat was sore, he sang beautifully.
   (3) Although she was upset, she smiled at him.

12 Peter made me sing in front of people though [although] I didn't want to.

13 (1) washed (2) taken (3) be read (4) reviewed

01 Though를 대신하여 Although, Even though 등을 써도 좋다.

02 목적어와 목적격 보어의 관계가 능동이므로 사역동사의 목적격 보어로 동사원형을 쓰는 것이 적절하다.

03 사역동사의 목적어와 목적격 보어의 관계가 능동 관계에 있을 경우 목적격 보어로 동사원형을, 수동 관계에 있을 경우 목적격 보어

로 과거분사를 쓴다. (1)은 to cross라고 써도 무방하다.

04 Although를 대신하여 다른 양보의 부사절 접속사를 사용해도 좋으며, 부사절을 주절 뒤로 배치할 경우 콤마를 쓰지 않는 것에 유의한다.

05 영화가 자신을 웃게 만들었다는 의미이다.

06 although와 even though는 접속사로서 주어와 동사를 포함하는 절을 이끌지만, despite은 전치사로 명사구를 이끄는 것에 유의한다.

07 사역동사 have, make, let은 목적어와 목적격 보어의 관계가 능동인 경우 목적격 보어로 동사원형을 쓴다.

08 양보의 부사절을 주절 뒤에 쓸 경우 콤마를 쓰지 않는다.

09 부모님이 내게 저녁에 운동을 하라고 시켰기 때문이라는 답이 가장 적절하다.

10 사역동사의 목적어와 목적격 보어의 관계가 능동인 경우 목적격 보어로 동사원형을 쓴다.

11 Although를 대신하여 Even though, Though를 써도 무방하며, 양보의 부사절을 주절 뒤에 쓸 경우 콤마를 쓰지 않는 것에 유의한다.

12 Peter는 내가 원하지 않았는데도 사람들 앞에서 노래하게 했다는 문장으로 쓸 수 있다.

13 사역동사 make, have의 목적어와 목적격 보어의 관계가 수동인 경우 목적격 보어로 과거분사를 쓴다. let은 be p.p.를 쓴다.

**교과서 Reading**

**확인문제**     p.80

1 T   2 F   3 T   4 F   5 T

**확인문제**     p.81

1 T   2 F   3 F   4 T   5 T

**교과서 확인학습 A**     p.82~83

01 floating village, middle
02 Although, never played soccer, watching it
03 decided to make
04 However, laughed at    05 impossible
06 makes, say so
07 Look around, to play
08 were right, to play soccer
09 discouraged   10 give up, still play soccer
11 How     12 make our own

13 gathered, pieces of
14 put, together, nailed, to
15 After much, had a floating field   16 shaky, nails
17 would often fall into, wet, slippery
18 no shoes, bare feet     19 they, care
20 In fact, excellent, enjoyed
21 brought a poster     22 decided to, it
23 When, were about to leave, them
24 made, feel    25 saw, as, weakest
26 However, started, surprised
27 On, was raining hard
28 losing by two goals, impossible to win
29 The other, so strong     30 give up
31 took off, during, changed completely
32 played better   33 lost by, to, proud of themselves
34 when they were losing, tried their best

**교과서 확인학습 B**     p.84~85

1 Koh Panyee was a small floating village in the middle of the sea.
2 Although the boys in the village never played soccer before, they loved watching it on TV.
3 One day, the boys decided to make their own soccer team.
4 However, people laughed at their idea.
5 "That's impossible."
6 "What makes you say so?"
7 "Look around. Where are you going to play soccer?"
8 The villagers were right. The boys had no place to play soccer.
9 They were discouraged.
10 "Don't give up! We can still play soccer."
11 "How?"
12 "Let's make our own soccer field."
13 The boys gathered old boats and pieces of wood.
14 They put the boats together and nailed the wood to them.
15 After much hard work, they finally had a floating field.
16 It was shaky and had nails everywhere.
17 The ball and the boys would often fall into the sea, so the field was always wet and slippery.
18 They had no shoes so they had to play in bare feet.
19 Still, they didn't care.
20 In fact, they built excellent skills and enjoyed playing soccer more.

21 One day, a boy brought a poster about a soccer tournament.

22 They decided to give it a try.

23 When they were about to leave, the villagers gave them new shoes and uniforms.

24 Some even came to watch the game. This made the boys feel better.

25 At first, people saw them as the weakest team.

26 However, when the tournament started, the soccer team surprised everyone.

27 On the day of the semi-final, it was raining hard.

28 They were losing by two goals and it looked impossible to win.

29 "The other team is so strong," they thought.

30 But the boys didn't give up.

31 They took off their shoes during the second half and the game changed completely.

32 They played better in the rain thanks to the slippery field at home.

33 Although they lost by a score of three to two, still, they felt proud of themselves.

34 They didn't give up when they were losing. They tried their best until the end.

## 시험대비 실력평가  p.86~.89

| | | | |
|---|---|---|---|
| 01 floating | 02 ③ | 03 ⑤ | 04 ② |
| 05 ⑤ | 06 slippery | 07 playing | 08 ② |
| 09 ④ | 10 ③ | 11 ⑤ | |

12 Although, give up  13 ③

14 매일 한 시간 동안 슛 연습을 한 것  15 shoot

16 ⑤  17 ⑤

18 They decided to make their own soccer team.

19 ⑤  20 ⑤  21 Though, built excellent skills  22 ⑤  23 ②

24 They gave shoes and uniforms to the boys.

25 It was raining hard on the day of the semi-final.

26 ⑤

01 '떠 있는'이라는 의미이므로 현재분사로 쓰는 것이 적절하다.

02 소년들이 축구팀을 만들기로 결심했지만 사람들이 그들의 생각을 비웃었다는 것이 적절하다.

03 소년들은 축구를 해 본 적은 없지만 TV로 축구를 보는 것은 정말 좋아했다고 하였다.

04 모두 소년들을 지칭하고 있지만 ②번은 boats를 가리키는 말이다.

05 소년들이 종종 바다에 빠졌고 축구장이 항상 젖어 있고 미끄럽다고 하였으므로 공중에 떠 있다는 설명은 적절하지 않다.

06 부드럽거나 젖어 있거나 얼음에 덮여 있어서, 움직이거나 혹은 붙잡고 있기 힘든 것은 'slippery(미끄러운)'이다.

07 enjoy는 동명사를 목적어로 취하는 동사이다.

08 This가 의미하는 것은 마을사람들이 소년들에게 새 신발과 축구복을 사주고 경기를 보러 온 것이다.

09 (A)는 '심하게, 많이'라는 의미의 부사로 쓰인 hard이다. ① 어려운, 힘든 ② (육체적, 정신적으로) 힘든 ③ 딱딱한 ④ 심하게, 많이 ⑤ 열심히 하는

10 due to = thanks to: ~ 덕분에, ~ 때문에

11 소년들이 몇 개의 경기를 했는지는 알 수 없다.

12 Although를 대신하여 Though 혹은 Even though를 써도 좋다. 소년들은 다른 팀이 매우 강하다고 생각했지만 포기하지 않았다.

13 다른 선수들과 달리 슛을 잘하지 못해 낙담했지만 포기하지 않았다는 의미가 자연스러우므로 discouraged가 적절하다.

14 앞 문장을 가리키고 있다.

15 사역동사 make의 목적어와 목적격 보어의 관계가 능동인 경우 목적격 보어로 동사원형을 쓴다.

16 (A)에는 전치사 at이 들어간다. laugh at: 비웃다 ① take care of: ~을 돌보다 ② be interested in: ~에 흥미가 있다 ③ give up: ~을 포기하다 ④ look forward to: ~을 고대하다 ⑤ be pleased at: ~에 기뻐하다

17 축구팀을 만들겠다는 결심을 비웃는 어른들의 말에 낙심했다는 것이 가장 자연스럽다. ① 고마워하는 ② 기쁜 ③ 지루한 ④ 놀란

18 소년들은 자신들의 축구팀을 만들기로 결심했다.

19 마을 사람들은 소년들의 의견을 지지해 주지 않았으며, 그 이유는 축구를 할 공간이 없었기 때문이었다. 소년들은 축구를 해 본 적은 없지만 텔레비전을 통해 축구를 보는 것을 즐겼다. 마을은 바다 한 가운데에 있었다.

20 축구장이 흔들린다고 하였으므로 '흔들림 없고 안정적인 (steady and stable)'이라고 생각한 Peter가 잘못 이해 했다.

21 양보의 부사절 접속사 Though를 대신하여 Although, Even though를 써도 좋다.

22 소년들이 낡은 배에 직접 못질을 하여 축구장을 만들었다.

23 축구 토너먼트에 참가해 보기로 한 것을 의미한다.

24 마을 사람들은 소년들에게 신발과 축구복을 주었다.

25 준결승전 날에 비가 심하게 오고 있었다고 하였다.

26 주어와 목적어가 같으므로 재귀대명사 themselves를 쓰는 것이 적절하다.

## 서술형 시험대비  p.90~91

01 making their own soccer team

02 It is in the middle of the sea.

03 Koh Panyee, playing it, make their own, despite

04 It's because the ball and the boys would often fall into the sea.

05 They gathered old boats and pieces of wood.

06 The floating field

07 Although there were no shoes, we didn't care.

08 Although

09 He brought a poster about a soccer tournament.

10 it looked impossible to win

11 They took off their shoes during the second half.

12 played better in the rain

13 ③번 → strong

14 Seeing them play in bare feet made Fern surprised.

15 become their fan

12 They will meet in front of the Student Center.

13 (C) → (B) → (E) → (D) → (A)

14 ⑤          15 ③          16 ④          17 ④

18 Although I was tired, I studied hard in class.

19 ④          20 ⑤

21 He missed the plane, he left early          22 ①, ③

23 ④          24 Although, drink

25 My parents don't let me watch violent movies.

26 ④          27 What makes you say so?

28 ③          29 (A) shooting (B) shoot          30 ④

31 ②, ③          32 ⑤

33 It's because they did not have shoes.

01 아이들이 자신의 축구팀을 만드는 것을 의미한다.

02 Koh Panyee 마을은 바다 가운데 있다고 하였다.

03 difficult conditions는 명사구이므로 전치사 despite을 쓰는 것에 유의한다. 해석: Koh Panyee라고 불리는 작은 마을에 사는 소년들은 축구를 보는 것을 아주 좋아하지만 그것을 해 본 경험은 없었다. 그래서, 어려운 조건에도 불구하고 그들은 자신들만의 축구팀을 만들기로 결심했다.

04 공과 소년들이 종종 바다에 빠져서 축구장이 항상 젖어 있고 미끄러웠다고 하였다.

05 소년들은 축구장을 만들기 위하여 낡은 배와 나뭇조각을 모았다.

06 소년들이 만든 물에 떠 있는 축구장을 가리킨다.

07 Though 혹은 Even though를 써도 좋다.

08 Even though, Though, While 모두 가능하다.

09 소년은 축구 토너먼트에 관한 포스터를 가지고 왔다.

10 가주어 it과 진주어 to부정사를 활용하여 문장을 쓸 수 있다.

11 후반전에 그들의 신발을 벗었다고 하였다.

12 고향의 미끄러운 축구장 때문에 그들은 빗속에서 더 잘하였다.

13 상대팀이 강했기 때문에 Panyee Soccer Team이 질 것이라고 생각했지만 그들이 포기하지 않았다는 것이 적절하다.

14 Fern은 선수들이 맨발로 경기하는 것을 보고 놀랐다고 하였다.

15 Koh Panyee 축구팀의 경기 중 하나를 본 것이 Fern Yahtie가 그들의 팬이 되게 하였다. 사역동사 make의 목적어와 목적격 보어의 관계가 능동이므로 목적격 보어로 동사원형을 쓴다.

### 영역별 핵심문제
p.93~97

01 impossible          02 ①          03 ④

04 (1) against (2) Although[Though] (3) bare (4) Still

05 ①          06 ①

07 (1) I felt proud of myself after the marathon race.
   (2) She walked in the woods in bare feet.
   (3) Don't be discouraged even if you lose.

08 ⓒ → haven't          09 ⑤          10 ⑤

11 It will be held on December 5th.

01 주어진 관계는 반의어 관계를 나타낸다. patient: 인내심이 있는, impatient: 참을성이 없는, impossible: 불가능한

02 축구 또는 농구 같은 운동에서 당신이 득점할 수 있는 곳을 향해 공을 차거나 던지다

03 villager: 마을 사람

04 against: ~에 맞서, although[though]: 비록 ~일지라도, bare: 맨..., 벌거벗은, proud: 자랑스러워하는

05 주어진 문장에서 match는 '경기, 시합'을 가리키며 이와 같은 의미로 쓰인 것은 ①번이다. ②, ③번은 '잘 어울리는 것 [사람]' ④, ⑤번은 '성냥'을 뜻한다.

06 주어진 문장에서 nail은 각각 '손톱', '못', '못을 박다'의 의미로 쓰였다.

07 proud 자랑스러워하는, bare 벌거벗은, 맨..., discouraged 낙담한

08 현재완료 시제로 알고 있는지 묻고 있으므로 'No, I haven't.'로 대답한다.

09 (A)에 들어갈 말로 격려하는 표현이 적절하다.

10 2004 유로컵에서 그리스 팀은 우승하였다.

11 "못생긴 스웨터 파티"는 12월 5일에 열릴 것이다.

12 소라와 Alex는 학생회관 앞에서 만날 것이다.

13 (C) 아이스하키 팀 지원에 확실하지 않음을 대답 → (B) 이유 질문 → (E) 이유 설명 → (D) 격려 및 응원하기 → (A) 대답 및 감사 표현

14 고민을 표현하고 조언을 구하는 질문에 '나는 최선을 다할 것이다'라는 대답은 어색하다.

15 사역동사 make의 목적어와 목적격 보어의 관계가 능동인 경우 목적격 보어로 동사원형을 쓴다.

16 모두 인과 관계를 연결하는 접속사 because나 as가 들어 가지만, ④번에는 양보의 부사절 접속사 although가 쓰인다.

17 '나는 그가 내 무거운 가방을 들게 했다.'이므로 '나는 내 무거운 가방이 그에 의해 들어지게 했다.'라고 쓸 수 있다.

18 Although를 대신하여 Even though, Though를 써도 좋다.

19 ① walk → to walk ② to wash → wash ③ Despite

→ Although[Though] ⑤ In spite → In spite of 혹은 Despite

20 get은 목적격 보어로 to부정사를 취하는 동사이다.

21 양보의 부사절 접속사가 이끄는 문장이 주절 뒤에 있을 때는 콤마를 쓰지 않는다.

22 help는 목적격 보어로 to부정사와 원형부정사를 모두 취할 수 있다.

23 날씨가 추웠지만 수영을 하러 갔다고 하였으므로 양보의 부사절 접속사가 적절하며, 목적격 보어로 동사원형을 취하고 있으므로 Let이 가장 적절하다.

24 Although를 대신하여 Though 혹은 Even though를 써도 좋다. 말이 물을 마시게 하는 것이므로 사역동사의 목적격 보어로 동사원형을 쓴다.

25 사역동사의 목적어와 목적격 보어의 관계가 능동이므로 목적격 보어로 동사원형을 쓴다.

26 축구를 할 장소가 없다고 하였으므로 ④번이 가장 적절하다.

27 사역동사 make의 목적어와 목적격 보어의 관계가 능동일 경우 목적격 보어로 동사원형을 쓴다.

28 소년들은 자신들의 축구장을 만들자고 하였으므로 ③번이 가장 적절하다.

29 (A) practice는 동명사를 목적어로 취하는 동사이다. (B) 사역동사의 목적어와 목적격 보어의 관계가 능동인 경우 목적격 보어로 동사원형을 쓴다.

30 글쓴이는 매일 한 시간 동안 슛 연습을 했다. 따라서 농구를 잘하기 위해서 열심히 노력했다는 것이 내용과 일치한다.

31 소년들은 실제로 훌륭한 기술을 쌓고 더 축구를 즐겼다는 것이 적절하다. Actually = In fact: 실제로, 사실

32 낡은 배와 나뭇조각들을 모은 소년들은 (C) 그것들을 합쳐서 축구장을 만들었다. (B) 그 축구장은 흔들리고 곳곳에 못이 있었다. 뿐만 아니라 축구장이 미끄럽고 맨발로 축구를 해야 했지만 (A) 소년들은 상관하지 않고 축구를 즐겼다.

33 소년들에게는 신발이 없었기 때문에 맨발로 축구를 해야 했다.

### 단원별 예상문제
p.98~101

01 (A) foot (B) 51 (C) to experience life in the desert (D) cross the desert on foot (E) try and cross the Gobi Desert in 50 days

02 ①　　03 ②　　04 match　　05 ⑤

06 ②　　07 ③　　08 ⑤

09 They tried out for the school ice hockey team.

10 He promised to try his best.

11 ⑤　　12 ④

13 Although the weather was very cold, she went out for a walk.

14 ⑤　　15 ①, ⑤　　16 take, taken

17 (B)–(A)–(C) 18 Although, surprised　　19 ④

---

20 ④　　　　21 They felt proud of themselves.

22 ⑤　　　　23 play better than before　24 ③

01 미나는 걸어서 고비 사막을 건너는 사람들에 대한 TV쇼를 보았다. 그것은 그들에게 약 51일 정도 걸렸다. 그녀는 흥미를 느꼈고 이것을 Tim에게 이야기했다. 그녀가 이것에 대해 설명했을 때, Tim도 또한 놀랐고 그는 사막에서의 삶을 경험해 보고 싶다고 이야기하였다. 하지만 Tim은 사막을 걸어서 건너고 싶지는 않았다. 반면에 용감한 마음을 지닌 미나는 시도해 보고 50일 안에 고비 사막을 건너고 싶어 했다.

02 미나는 사막 생활 경험을 시도해 보고 고비 사막을 50일 내로 건너고 싶어 하므로 용감한(brave)이 적절하다. thoughtful: 사려 깊은, polite: 예의바른, shy: 수줍어하는, honest: 정직한

03 주어진 문장은 알고 있는지 여부를 묻는 질문에 대한 대답으로 적절하므로 (B)가 알맞다.

04 '둘 또는 그 이상의 선수들이나 팀들 간의 경쟁'을 가리키는 말은 match(경기)이다.

05 위 대화를 통해 Emily가 게임에 이기기 위해 무엇을 했는지는 알 수 없다.

07 나머지는 모두 고비 사막을 가리키지만, ⓒ는 비인칭 용법이다.

08 Tim은 왜 걸어서 고비 사막을 건너고 싶지 않은지 대화를 통해 알 수 없다.

09 Tony와 Brad는 학교 아이스하키 팀에 지원했다.

10 호준은 최선을 다할 것을 약속했다.

11 여권 사진이 필요했지만 사진을 잘 찍는 방법을 모르는 남동생이 사진을 찍게 했다는 의미이다. 사역동사의 목적어와 목적격 보어의 관계가 수동이므로 taken이 적절하다.

12 사역동사 let의 목적격 보어로 동사원형을 쓰는 것이 적절하다. shoe polish: 구두 광택제

13 Although를 대신하여 Even though 혹은 Though를 써도 좋다.

14 get은 목적격 보어로 to부정사를 취하는 동사이다.

15 ② Despite → Although ③ because → though ④ brought → bring

16 사역동사 have의 목적어와 목적격 보어의 관계가 능동인 경우 목적격 보어로 동사원형을, 수동인 경우 과거분사를 쓴다.

17 한 소년이 축구 토너먼트에 관한 포스터를 가지고 왔고 (B) 소년들은 한번 해 보기로 결정함. 떠나려고 할 때 마을 사람들이 새 신발과 축구복을 주었고, (A) 몇몇 사람들은 경기를 보러 오기도 함. 사람들은 소년들을 가장 약한 팀으로 보았음. (C) 하지만 토너먼트가 시작되자 사람들은 놀람.

18 비록 사람들은 그 팀이 가장 약한 팀일 것이라고 생각했지만, 토너먼트가 시작되었을 때 그들은 그 팀에 놀랐다.

19 두 골 '차이'로 지고 있었다는 의미이다. 정도나 비율의 차이를 나타내며 '~만큼'이라는 의미로 쓰이는 전치사는 by이다.

20 고향의 미끄러운 축구장 덕분에 빗속에서 경기를 더 잘하였다. 준결승전 날에 비가 심하게 내렸고, 소년들은 두 골 차로 지고 있었으

며 후반전에 신발을 벗고 경기를 뛰었지만 3대 2로 지고 말았다.

21 소년들은 스스로를 자랑스럽게 여겼다.

22 주어와 동사를 포함하는 절을 이끌고 있으므로 Although를 쓰는 것이 적절하다. Despite은 명사구를 이끄는 전치사이다.

23 Fern은 선수들이 맨발로 경기를 한 것이 선수들이 경기를 더 잘하게 만들었다고 생각했다. 사역동사 make의 목적어와 목적격 보어의 관계가 능동이므로 목적격 보어로 play를 쓴다.

24 후반전 동안 선수들은 맨발로 경기를 하였다. 따라서 신발을 신지 않고 경기에 임했다는 ③번이 글의 내용과 일치한다.

10 앞에서 언급한 내용과 상반되는 내용을 추가할 때 쓰는 말로 However가 적절하다.

11 그들만의 축구장을 만든 후, 비록 축구장이 흔들리고 맨발로 축구를 해야 하지만 소년들은 행복하다.

12 take part in: ~에 참가하다

13 3대 2로 졌다고 하였으므로 그 팀은 결국 2점을 얻었다고 할 수 있다.

14 hardly는 부사로 '거의 … 아니다[않다]'라는 의미이고 hard는 부사로 '몹시, 심하게'라는 의미이다.

15 though, even though를 써도 무방하다.

16 고향에 있는 미끄러운 축구장이 그들을 빗속에서 더 잘하게 하였다.

---

### 서술형 실전문제    p.102~103

01 have you heard of the Gobi Desert?
02 It took them about 51 days.
03 She wants to try and cross the Gobi Desert in 50 days.
04 Although[Though] he doesn't have time, he tries to exercise every day.
05 had me write, made me clean
06 Though I was very tired, I stayed up late.
07 shortened
08 made me feel sorry
09 A Soccer Team with Courage
10 However
11 it is shaky and they play in bare feet
12 they take part in a tournament
13 The team got two goals in the end.
14 hardly → hard
15 although
16 play better in the rain

02 약 51일이 걸렸다.

03 미나는 시도해 보고 고비 사막을 50일 내로 건너고 싶어 한다.

04 양보의 부사절 Although가 이끄는 문장을 주절 뒤에 쓰면 콤마를 쓰지 않는 것에 유의한다.

05 사역동사의 목적어와 목적격 보어의 관계가 능동이므로 목적격 보어로 동사원형을 쓴다. 과거에 일어난 일이므로 모두 과거시제를 쓴다.

06 Though를 대신하여 Although 혹은 Even though를 써도 무방하다.

07 사역동사 have의 목적어와 목적격 보어의 관계가 수동이므로 과거분사를 목적격 보어로 쓴다. shorten: 짧게 하다

08 '내가 미안함을 느끼게 하는' 것이므로 사역동사의 목적격 보어로 동사원형을 쓴다.

09 포기하지 않고 도전하는 소년들에 관한 이야기이므로 '용기 있는 축구팀'이 가장 적절하다.

---

### 창의사고력 서술형 문제    p.104

01 (A) the school ice hockey team
　 (B) Tony and Brad
　 (C) give up
　 (D) try my best

|모범답안|

02 (1) My brother made me clean his room.
　 (2) My dad let me go out with my friends.
　 (3) The teacher had us do the project together.
　 (4) My friend made me take her umbrella.

01 나는 학교 아이스하키 팀에 지원할지 고민하고 있었다. 사실, 나는 자신감이 없었다. 왜냐하면 Tony와 Brad가 아이스하키 팀에 지원했다고 들었기 때문이다. 나는 그들이 굉장히 잘하는 선수들이라는 것을 알았다. 내가 수지와 이야기했을 때, 그녀는 내가 포기하지 않도록 격려해 주었다. 그녀는 나도 아이스하키를 잘한다고 말했다. 나는 그녀에게 최선을 다할 것을 약속했다.

---

### 단원별 모의고사    p.105~108

01 ⑤     02 (1) semi-final (2) shaky (3) shoot
03 ②     04 ③     05 ③     06 ⑤
07 (1) It was shaky and had nails everywhere.
　 (2) The boys gathered old boats and pieces of wood.
08 Tony and Brad are also trying out for the team
09 ②     10 ③
11 They played as a team and worked hard.
12 (A) the Greek team (B) give up (C) Saturday
　 (D) try her best
13 repaired by Tom     14 ⑤     15 ③
16 ④     17 ④     18 bare     19 ⑤
20 ③     21 ④
22 They decided to give it a try.
23 Although it looked impossible to win, we didn't give up.

01 '일반적으로 노력, 용기 또는 기술에 의해 성공적으로 이루어진 것'을 가리키는 말은 achievement(성취)이다.

02 semi-final: 준결승전, shaky: 흔들리는, shoot: 슛하다

03 (A) try out for 지원하다, (B) give up 포기하다, (C) take off 벗다

04 (C) 다음 문장의 it이 주어진 문장의 one을 가리키므로 (C)가 적절하다.

05 Alex는 소라가 입지 않는 스웨터를 입을 것이다.

06 위 대화를 통해 건강해지기 위해 어느 조언이 가장 중요한지는 알 수 없다.

07 everywhere: 모든 곳에, gather: 모으다

09 (A)는 확실하지 않다는 말이 자연스러우므로 sure, (B) '포기하다'는 give up, (C) '최선을 다하다'를 의미하는 try one's best가 적절하다.

10 ©를 제외한 나머지는 모두 the Greek team을 가리킨다.

11 비록 그리스 팀은 약팀이었지만 한 팀으로 경기하며 열심히 했기 때문에 2004 유로컵에서 우승할 수 있었다.

12 Emily의 아빠는 Emily에게 어떻게 그리스 팀이 2004 유로컵에서 이겼는지 이야기했다. 왜냐하면 그녀의 아빠는 그녀가 토요일에 있는 경기를 포기하기를 원하지 않았기 때문이다. 아빠와 이야기한 후, Emily는 최선을 다할 것을 결심했다.

13 신발은 수리되는 것이므로 과거분사로 쓰는 것이 적절하다.

14 ① crying → cry ② Despite → Although ③ ran → run ④ 주절 앞에 콤마를 써야 함.

15 아이들이 도와주도록 시킨 것이므로 첫 번째 빈칸에는 help이며 help의 목적격 보어로 to부정사나 동사원형이 모두 올 수 있으므로 ③번이 적절하다.

16 공과 소년들이 종종 바다에 빠져서 축구장이 항상 젖어 있고 미끄러웠다고 하는 것이 자연스럽다.

17 소년들은 망치질을 직접 하였다.

18 옷, 신발, 모자 등에 의해서 덮이지 않은 것은 '벌거벗은, 맨-(bare)'이다.

19 소년들이 축구팀을 만들겠다는 말에 사람들이 비웃었다고 하였으므로, 소년들이 축구팀을 만들도록 장려했다는 ⑤번은 글의 내용과 일치하지 않는다.

20 (A)는 to부정사의 형용사적 용법으로 쓰였다. ① 명사적 용법 중 목적격 보어 ② 진주어 ③ 형용사적 용법 ④ 부사적 용법 중 목적 ⑤ 명사적 용법 중 목적어

21 모두 소년들을 지칭하고 있지만 ④번은 마을 사람들을 가리킨다.

22 소년들은 축구 토너먼트에 관한 포스터를 본 후 한번 해 보기로 결정했다.

23 Although 대신 Though, Even though를 써도 무방하며, 양보의 부사절을 주절 뒤에 쓸 경우 콤마를 쓰지 않는다.

# 교과서 파헤치기

## Lesson 7

### 단어 TEST Step 1                                             p.02

| | | |
|---|---|---|
| 01 맛 | 02 안전한 | 03 차이, 차이점 |
| 04 탈출하다, (액체, 가스가) 새다 | | 05 채우다 |
| 06 냉동고 | 07 대신에 | 08 가라앉다 |
| 09 뜨다 | 10 번개 | 11 압력 |
| 12 비밀 | 13 ~ 뒤에 | 14 준비하다 |
| 15 볕에 탐 | 16 팽창하다 | 17 마술, 속임수 |
| 18 재료, 물질 | 19 비교하다 | 20 흡수하다 |
| 21 불꽃 | 22 수축하다 | 23 사라지다 |
| 24 실험 | 25 마른, 비가 오지 않는 | |
| 26 혼동하게 하다 | 27 오르다, 올라가다 | 28 무게를 재다 |
| 29 마술, 마법 | 30 자외선 차단제 | 31 잡다, 쥐다 |
| 32 양초 | 33 연습 | 34 필요한 |
| 35 오랫동안 | 36 차가워지다 | 37 ~을 신청하다 |
| 38 시도해 보다 | 39 ~을 (바꾸지 않고) 고수하다 | |
| 40 타 버리다 | 41 골라내다 | 42 속을 들여다 보다 |
| 43 A가 B로 변하다 | | |

### 단어 TEST Step 2                                             p.03

| | | |
|---|---|---|
| 01 coin | 02 fill | 03 practice |
| 04 magic | 05 disappear | 06 dry |
| 07 expand | 08 candle | 09 sunburn |
| 10 flavor | 11 sink | 12 absorb |
| 13 secret | 14 instead | 15 lightning |
| 16 material | 17 sunscreen | 18 difference |
| 19 contract | 20 mix | 21 experiment |
| 22 necessary | 23 safe | 24 trick |
| 25 flame | 26 prepare | 27 confuse |
| 28 float | 29 escape | 30 compare |
| 31 pressure | 32 weigh | 33 rise |
| 34 freezer | 35 pick out | 36 burn out |
| 37 stick to | 38 for a long time | 39 cool down |
| 40 turn A into B | 41 sign up for | 42 give it a try |
| 43 see through | | |

### 단어 TEST Step 3                                             p.04

1 disappear, 사라지다   2 contract, 수축하다
3 mix, 섞다   4 sink, 가라앉다   5 expand, 팽창하다
6 float, 뜨다   7 confuse, 혼동하게 하다
8 material, 물질, 재료   9 trick, 속임수, 마술
10 freezer, 냉동고   11 weigh, 무게를 재다

12 absorb, 흡수하다   13 magic, 마술의
14 experiment, 실험   15 secret, 비밀
16 practice, 연습

### 대화문 TEST Step 1                                            p.05~06

**Listen & Speak 1 A**

Which flavor, How about, First, half a cup, Next, cut, into, mix, freezer, easy to make, isn't, Why don't, try making

**Listen & Speak 1 B**

why, put / picking out / Which eggs, which / that sink in water, float, shouldn't eat / interesting, float / Because, inside, acts like, balloon

**Listen & Speak 2 A**

a glass of, weigh / can test / fish / can use, instead of / How, work / weigh, put / weigh, compare / can't wait to, difference

**Listen & Speak 2 B**

hasn't rained for / dry season, lasting, worried / should, to help / special clock / How, help / seasons, to prepare for, dry season / sounds like, going to / give it a try, a lot / can't wait to see your clock

**Real Life Communication A**

join / sounds interesting, signed up for, fall / Which class / magic class, can't wait to, tricks / cool, Have you learned / more practice / some day

**Let's Check**

are, reading / magic, science / sounds, interesting / introduces, use science, learned about half / cool, some / balloon trick / can't wait to see

### 대화문 TEST Step 2                                            p.07~08

**Listen & Speak 1 A**

W: Today we'll make ice cream. Which flavor do you want to make? How about strawberry? First, mix two cups of milk, two cups of heavy cream, and half a cup of sugar. Next, cut five strawberries into small pieces. Then, mix everything together and put it in the freezer. That's it. It's easy to make, isn't it? Why don't you try making it at home?

**Listen & Speak 1 B**

B: Yujin, why did you put the eggs in water?
G: I'm picking out the bad eggs.
B: Which eggs are fresh, and which ones are not?

G: Eggs that sink in water are fresh. When eggs float in water, they're not fresh. You shouldn't eat them.

B: That's interesting. Why do the bad eggs float?

G: Because they have gas inside. The gas acts like the air in a balloon.

B: Oh, I see.

### Listen & Speak 2 A

B: Ms. Jeong, does a glass of water weigh more when there's a fish in it?

W: Yes, it does. We can test it now.

B: But how? We don't have a fish.

W: We can use a finger instead of a fish.

B: How will that work?

W: I'll weigh a glass of water first. Then I will put my finger in the water and weigh it to compare.

B: Oh, I can't wait to see the difference.

### Listen & Speak 2 B

King Sejong: It hasn't rained for a long time.

Jang Yeongsil: Yes. The dry season is lasting too long. The farmers are very worried.

King Sejong: We should do something to help them.

Jang Yeongsil: How about making a special clock?

King Sejong: A clock? How will that help?

Jang Yeongsil: The clock will show the time and the seasons. We can use it to prepare for the dry season.

King Sejong: That sounds like a good idea. But who's going to make it?

Jang Yeongsil: I'll give it a try. I know a lot about time and the seasons.

King Sejong: Okay, I can't wait to see your clock.

### Real Life Communication A

Brian: Mina, will you join our tennis club?

Mina: It sounds interesting, but I signed up for a special class this fall.

Brian: Which class did you sign up for?

Mina: I signed up for a magic class. I can't wait to learn new magic tricks there.

Brian: That sounds cool! Have you learned magic tricks before?

Mina: Yes, I learned some before, but I need more practice.

Brian: I hope I can see your magic tricks some day.

### Let's Check

B: What are you reading, Jiwon?

G: I'm reading a book about magic and science.

B: That sounds interesting.

G: Yes. This book introduces 100 magic tricks that

use science. I've learned about half of them.

B: That's cool. Can you show me some of the tricks?

G: Sure. I can show you a balloon trick now.

B: Great! I can't wait to see it.

### 본문 TEST Step 1 p.09~10

01 Welcome to, Super, Magic
02 It's, exciting, see, tricks
03 more, find out, behind
04 secret, magic, science
05 member, science, perform, tricks
06 show, can't wait
07 show, something amazing
08 dish with water
09 put, middle, dish
10 light, cover, with
11 How come, rose into
12 expands, hot, higher pressure
13 gets, contracts, lower pressure
14 burnt out, lower pressure
15 cooled, pressure dropped
16 outside, higher pressure
17 pushed, water, glass
18 fill one, with water
19 move, around, confuse
20 which cup, water
21 easy, middle one          22 let's check
23 me the other cups
24 There's no water
25 How come, disappeared
26 Before, put, into, cups
27 absorbed, turned, into
28 stuck to, bottom
29 try, necessary, use, through
30 for, performance, amazing

### 본문 TEST Step 2 p.11~12

01 Welcome to, Science Magic
02 It's, exciting to see
03 to find out, behind
04 secret, is science
05 will use science to perform, tricks
06 will, show us, wait to see them
07 to show you something amazing

08 with water in it

09 put a candle, middle

10 light, cover it with

11 Look at, How come, rose into

12 expands, gets hot, creates higher pressure

13 gets cold, contracts, creates lower pressure

14 burnt out, lower pressure

15 cooled down, dropped

16 outside, was at a higher pressure

17 pushed, into

18 going to fill one of these cups with

19 them around to confuse

20 which cup    21 It's, middle one

22 let's check    23 me the other cups

24 no water    25 How come, disappeared

26 Before, put, into one of the cups

27 absorbed, turned it into

28 stuck to the bottom

29 want to try, necessary to use, that, see through

30 for, performance, amazing

---

1 지나: 특별 과학 마술 쇼에 오신 것을 환영합니다!

2 마술을 보는 것은 항상 신나는 일입니다.

3 그리고 마술 뒤에 숨겨진 비밀을 알아내는 것은 더 신나는 일입니다.

4 어떤 사람들은 마술의 비밀이 과학이라고 생각합니다.

5 오늘 학교 마술 동아리 회원인 Ken은 마술을 수행하기 위해 과학을 사용할 것입니다.

6 그는 우리에게 어떤 마술을 보여 줄까요? 무척 기다려지는군요.

7 Ken: 안녕하세요, 여러분. 오늘, 저는 여러분에게 놀라운 무언가를 보여 주려고 합니다.

8 여기에 물이 담긴 접시가 있습니다.

9 이제, 저는 접시 한가운데에 초를 놓을 것입니다.

10 그다음에 초를 켜고 유리컵으로 초를 덮어 보겠습니다. "아브라카다브라!"

11 지나: 물을 보세요! 어째서 물이 유리컵 속으로 올라간 거지요?

12 Ken: 공기가 뜨거워지면 팽창해서, 더 높은 압력을 만듭니다.

13 공기가 차가워지면 수축해서, 더 낮은 압력을 만듭니다.

14 불꽃이 다 타 버렸을 때, 유리컵 속의 공기는 식어 버렸습니다.

15 공기가 식었으므로, 기압이 낮아졌습니다.

16 그래서 유리컵 밖의 공기 압력이 더 높아졌습니다.

17 높아진 압력의 공기가 물을 밀어서 유리컵으로 들어가게 된 것입니다.

18 Ken: 이제, 이 컵들 중 하나를 물로 채워 보겠습니다.

19 여러분을 헷갈리게 하려고 이 컵들을 섞어 보겠습니다.

---

20 지나, 어떤 컵에 물이 있을까요?

21 지나: 쉽네요! 가운데 컵이에요.

22 Ken: 좋습니다, 확인해 봅시다. 보셨죠? 물이 없군요.

23 지나: 다른 컵들도 보여 주세요.

24 Ken: 보셨죠? 물이 없네요.

25 지나: 와! 어째서 물이 사라진 거죠?

26 Ken: 마술 전에, 저는 특별한 물질을 컵 하나에 넣어 두었습니다.

27 그 물질은 물을 흡수하고, 그것을 젤리로 변하게 했습니다.

28 그러고 나서 젤리는 컵 바닥에 달라붙었습니다.

29 여러분이 이 마술을 해 보고자 한다면, 속을 들여다볼 수 없는 컵을 사용해야 합니다.

30 지나: 멋진 공연 고맙습니다. 정말 놀라웠어요!

---

1 Jina: Welcome to the Super Science Magic Show!

2 It's always exciting to see magic tricks.

3 And it's more exciting to find out the secrets behind them.

4 Some people think the secret of magic is science.

5 Today, Ken, a member of the School Magic Club, will use science to perform his tricks.

6 Which tricks will he show us? I can't wait to see them.

7 Ken: Hello, everyone. Today, I'm going to show you something amazing.

8 Here's a dish with water in it.

9 Now, I'll put a candle in the middle of the dish.

10 Next, I'll light the candle and cover it with a glass. "Abracadabra!"

11 Jina: Look at the water! How come it rose into the glass?

12 Ken: Air expands when it gets hot and creates higher pressure.

13 When it gets cold, air contracts and creates lower pressure.

14 When the flame burnt out, the air inside the glass cooled down.

15 As the air cooled down, the air pressure dropped.

16 So the air outside the glass was at a higher pressure.

17 It pushed the water into the glass.

18 Ken: Now, I'm going to fill one of these cups with water.

19 I will move them around to confuse you.

20 Jina, which cup has the water in it?

---

21 Jina: That's easy! It's the middle one.

22 Ken: Okay, let's check. See? No water.

23 Jina: Show me the other cups.

24 Ken: See? There's no water.

25 Jina: Wow! How come the water disappeared?

26 Ken: Before the trick, I put a special material into one of the cups.

27 The material absorbed the water and turned it into jelly.

28 Then the jelly stuck to the bottom.

29 If you want to try this trick, it's necessary to use cups that you can't see through.

30 Jina: Thank you for your great performance. It was really amazing!

4. It's still a mystery.

### Culture & Life

1. Egypt – The pyramids

2. Some of the rocks that were used to build the pyramids weigh about 70 tons.

3. How was it possible to move such heavy rocks back then?

4. It's still a mystery.

---

## 구석구석지문 TEST Step 1                          p.19

### Real Life Communication B

1. Which class, sign up for

2. take, class, like playing, about

3. take the computer class, can't wait to

4. sounds

### Culture & Life

1. Atlantic Ocean, Triangle

2. A number of, have disappeared

3. come

4. still

### Culture & Life

1. Egypt

2. that were used to build, weigh about

3. it possible to move

4. still a mystery

---

## 구석구석지문 TEST Step 2                          p.20

### Real Life Communication B

1. A: Which class do you want to sign up for ?

2. B: I want to take the badminton class. I like playing badminton. How about you?

3. A: I want to take the computer class. I can't wait to make a computer program there.

4. B: That sounds cool!

### Culture & Life

1. North Atlantic Ocean – The Bermuda Triangle

2. A number of airplanes and ships have disappeared in the Bermuda Triangle.

3. How come?

13 proud, 자랑스러워하는  14 slippery, 미끄러운

15 courage, 용기  16 shoot, 슛하다

## 단어 TEST Step 1                                    p.21

01 미끄러운    02 넓은        03 벌거벗은, 맨 ~
04 모든 곳에, 어디나  05 마을    06 흔들리는 휘청거리는
07 못생긴, 추한    08 훌륭한    09 경험하다
10 걱정하다, 관심을 갖다        11 떠 있는
12 모으다, 모이다  13 건강한    14 ~에 맞서
15 불가능한    16 용기        17 경기
18 식사, 끼니    19 성과        20 못질하다; 못
21 운동하다    22 자랑스러워하는  23 준결승전
24 낙담한      25 약한        26 놀라운
27 소리 지르다, 소리치다        28 비록 ~일지라도
29 토너먼트    30 마을 사람    31 완전히
32 지다, 잃다   33 결정하다, 결심하다
34 바람이 센    35 ~에 빠지다   36 최선을 다하다
37 걸어서, 도보로  38 ~을 지원하다  39 시도해 보다
40 사실은      41 막 ~하려고 하다  42 포기하다
43 ~을 비웃다

## 단어 TEST Step 2                                    p.22

01 shout       02 although    03 care
04 shaky       05 completely  06 discouraged
07 slippery    08 decide      09 nail
10 everywhere  11 wide        12 experience
13 floating    14 achievement 15 excellent
16 against     17 gather      18 match
19 healthy     20 shoot       21 weak
22 bare        23 impossible  24 villager
25 lose        26 courage     27 amazing
28 windy       29 meal        30 ugly
31 proud       32 semi-final  33 exercise
34 wash        35 in fact     36 on foot
37 give it a try  38 laugh at
39 try[do] one's best          40 give up
41 be about to  42 fall into  43 be good at

## 단어 TEST Step 3                                    p.23

1 excellent, 훌륭한  2 weak, 약한  3 lose, 지다
4 bare, 벌거벗은  5 shout, 소리치다  6 villager, 마을 사람
7 shaky, 흔들리는, 휘청거리는  8 match, 경기
9 nail, 못질하다  10 achievement, 성과
11 gather, 모으다  12 discouraged, 낙담한

## 대화문 TEST Step 1                                  p.24~25

**Listen & Speak 1 A**

have you heard of / have, Isn't, in / saw, who crossed, on  foot / Only / took, about / to experience life, desert, cross, on foot / try, cross, in

**Listen & Speak 1 B**

have you heard about / course, have, on, right / right, going to / want to / I don't wear at home, if you want / would / Let's meet in front of, go inside / Sure, See

**Listen & Speak 2 A**

healthy, exercise, try to eat healthy food, Don't eat, wash, meals, sound hard, take, step at a time, give up, live, life

**Listen & Speak 2 B**

try out for, is about to / sure / Why not / heard, trying out for / good at, don't give up / try my best, a lot

**Real Life Communication**

excited, match / against, lost / Don't say, Have you heard about / No, haven't, about / so, thought, lose / What happened / as. worked hard, won, give up / try our best

**Let's Check ❶**

Have you heard of, When, couldn't read well, lost, hearing in, Still, Although, difficulties, be like, don't give up

## 대화문 TEST Step 2                                  p.26~27

**Listen & Speak 1 A**

G: Tim, have you heard of the Gobi Desert?

B: Yes, I have. Isn't it in Mongolia and China?

G: Yes, it is. Yesterday, I saw a TV show about people who crossed the desert on foot.

B: Only on foot?

G: Yes, it took them about 51 days.

B: Wow, that's amazing. I want to experience life in the desert but I don't want to cross it on foot.

G: Well, I want to try and cross the Gobi Desert in 50 days.

**Listen & Speak 1 B**

G: Alex, have you heard about this year's "Ugly Sweater Party?"

B: Of course, I have. It's on December 5th, right?

G: That's right. Are you going to go?

B: I want to, but I don't have an ugly sweater.

G: I have one that I don't wear at home. You can have it if you want.

B: Thanks. That would be great.

G: Let's meet in front of the Student Center and go inside together.

B: Sure. See you then.

### Listen & Speak 2 A

W: What can you do to be healthy? First, try to exercise every day. Second, try to eat healthy food. Don't eat too much fast food. Third, wash your hands before meals. Do these tips sound hard to do? Well, take one step at a time and don't give up. Then you'll live a healthy life.

### Listen & Speak 2 B

G: Hojun, are you going to try out for the school ice hockey team? The new season is about to start.

B: I'm not sure.

G: Why not?

B: I heard that Tony and Brad are also trying out for the team. They're so good.

G: Well, you're also good at ice hockey, so don't give up!

B: Okay, I'll try my best. Thanks a lot.

### Real Life Communication

Father: Emily, are you excited about your match on Saturday?

Emily: Not really. We're playing against a strong team. I think we'll lose.

Father: Don't say that. Have you heard about the Greek team in the 2004 Euro Cup?

Emily: No, I haven't. What about them?

Father: They were a weak team, so everyone thought that they would lose.

Emily: What happened?

Father: They played as a team and worked hard. Finally, they won the Euro Cup. So, don't give up.

Emily: Thanks, Dad. We'll try our best.

### Let's Check ❶

B: Have you heard of Thomas Edison? When he was young, he couldn't read well. Also, he lost all of the hearing in his left ear. Still, he became a great scientist. Although you may have difficulties, be like Edison and don't give up.

01 floating village, middle
02 Although, never played, watching
03 decided to make, own
04 However, laughed at
05 That's impossible          06 makes, say so
07 Look around, going, play
08 villagers, right, place to
09 were discouraged
10 give up, still play
12 Let's, own, field
13 gathered, pieces of
14 put, together, nailed, to
15 After, work, finally, floating
16 shaky, nails everywhere
17 fall into, wet, slippery
18 no shoes, bare feet          19 Still, care
20 In fact, excellent, enjoyed
21 One, brought, poster, tournament
22 decided to, it, try
23 When, about, leave, shoes
24 even, made, feel better
25 At, saw, as, weakest
26 However, started, surprised
27 On, semi-final, raining hard
28 losing by, impossible, win
29 other, strong, thought          30 didn't give up
31 took off, during, completely
32 better, thanks to, slippery
33 by, to, proud of
34 give, losing, tried, until

01 a small floating village, middle
02 Although, never played soccer, watching it on TV
03 One day, decided to make
04 However, laughed at their idea
05 impossible          06 makes, say so
07 Look around, are, going to play
08 were right, no place to play soccer
09 were discouraged
10 give up, still play soccer          11 How
12 Let's make our own
13 gathered, pieces of wood
14 put, together, nailed, to
15 After much, finally had a floating field

25

16 shaky, had nails everywhere

17 would often fall into, always wet, slippery

18 no shoes, had to, bare feet    19 Still, they, care

20 In fact, excellent, enjoyed playing

21 brought a poster

22 decided to, it, try

23 When, were about to leave, them new shoes

24 made, feel better

25 saw, as, weakest

26 However, when, started, surprised everyone

27 On, was raining hard

28 losing by two goals, impossible to win

29 The other, so strong    30 But, give up

31 took off, during, second half, changed completely

32 played better, thanks to

33 Although, lost by, to, proud of themselves

34 give up when they were losing, tried their best

---

24 몇몇은 심지어 경기를 보러 왔다. 이것은 소년들의 기분을 더 좋게 만들었다.

25 처음에, 사람들은 그들을 가장 약한 팀으로 보았다.

26 그러나 토너먼트가 시작되었을 때, 그 축구팀은 모든 사람들을 놀라게 했다.

27 준결승전 날, 비가 심하게 오고 있었다.

28 그들은 두 골 차로 지고 있었고, 이기는 것은 불가능해 보였다.

29 "다른 팀이 아주 강해."라고 그들은 생각했다.

30 그러나 소년들은 포기하지 않았다.

31 그들은 후반전에 그들의 신발을 벗었고 경기는 완전히 바뀌었다.

32 고향의 미끄러운 축구장 덕분에 그들은 빗속에서 더 잘하였다.

33 비록 그들은 3대 2로 졌지만, 그들은 그들 자신이 자랑스러웠다.

34 그들은 그들이 지고 있을 때 포기하지 않았다. 그들은 끝까지 최선을 다하였다.

---

본문 TEST Step 4-Step 5                p.34~37

1 Koh Panyee was a small floating village in the middle of the sea.

2 Although the boys in the village never played soccer before, they loved watching it on TV.

3 One day, the boys decided to make their own soccer team.

4 However, people laughed at their idea.

5 "That's impossible."

6 "What makes you say so?"

7 "Look around. Where are you going to play soccer?"

8 The villagers were right. The boys had no place to play soccer.

9 They were discouraged.

10 "Don't give up! We can still play soccer."

11 "How?"

12 "Let's make our own soccer field."

13 The boys gathered old boats and pieces of wood.

14 They put the boats together and nailed the wood to them.

15 After much hard work, they finally had a floating field.

16 It was shaky and had nails everywhere.

17 The ball and the boys would often fall into the sea, so the field was always wet and slippery.

18 They had no shoes so they had to play in bare feet.

19 Still, they didn't care.

20 In fact, they built excellent skills and enjoyed playing soccer more.

---

본문 TEST Step 3                p.32~33

1 Koh Panyee는 바다 가운데 떠 있는 작은 수상 마을이었다.

2 비록 그 마을의 소년들은 이전에 축구를 해 본 적이 없었지만, 그들은 그것을 TV로 보는 것을 정말 좋아했다.

3 어느 날, 그 소년들은 그들만의 축구팀을 만들기로 하였다.

4 그러나 사람들은 그들의 생각을 비웃었다.

5 "그것은 불가능해."

6 "왜 그렇게 말하는 거죠?"

7 "주위를 둘러봐. 너희는 어디서 축구를 할 거니?"

8 마을 사람들이 옳았다. 소년들은 축구를 할 장소가 없었다.

9 그들은 낙담했다.

10 "포기하지 마! 우리는 여전히 축구를 할 수 있어."

11 "어떻게?"

12 "우리만의 축구장을 만들자."

13 소년들은 낡은 배와 나뭇조각들을 모았다.

14 그들은 배를 합치고 그것들 위에 나무를 못으로 박았다.

15 매우 열심히 일한 후, 그들은 마침내 떠 있는 축구장을 가지게 되었다.

16 그것은 흔들리고 곳곳에 못이 있었다.

17 공과 소년들은 종종 바다에 빠졌고, 축구장은 항상 젖어 있고 미끄러웠다.

18 그들은 신발이 없어서 맨발로 축구를 해야 했다.

19 그런데도 그들은 상관하지 않았다.

20 실제로 그들은 훌륭한 기술을 쌓았고 더욱 더 축구를 즐겼다.

21 어느 날, 한 소년이 축구 토너먼트에 관한 포스터를 가지고 왔다.

22 그들은 한번 해 보기로 결정했다.

23 그들이 떠나려고 할 때, 마을 사람들은 그들에게 새 신발과 축구복을 주었다.

21 One day, a boy brought a poster about a soccer tournament.

22 They decided to give it a try.

23 When they were about to leave, the villagers gave them new shoes and uniforms.

24 Some even came to watch the game. This made the boys feel better.

25 At first, people saw them as the weakest team.

26 However, when the tournament started, the soccer team surprised everyone.

27 On the day of the semi-final, it was raining hard.

28 They were losing by two goals and it looked impossible to win.

29 "The other team is so strong," they thought.

30 But the boys didn't give up.

31 They took off their shoes during the second half and the game changed completely.

32 They played better in the rain thanks to the slippery field at home.

33 Although they lost by a score of three to two, still, they felt proud of themselves.

34 They didn't give up when they were losing. They tried their best until the end.

구석구석지문 TEST Step 1                                     p.38

**Real Life Communication - Step 2**

1. want to be, but, too short, give up

2. don't give up, Have, heard of

3. haven't

4. basketball player, short, won

**Culture & Life**

1. from, surprised, whole world

2. Although, only a month to prepare, won, at

**Let's Write**

1. My favorite sport

2. However, wasn't, good at

3. unlike other players

4. felt discouraged, give up

5. practiced, for an hour every day

6. made me shoot, the best player

구석구석지문 TEST Step 2                                     p.39

**Real Life Communication - Step 2**

1. A: I want to be a basketball player but I'm too short. Should I give up?

2. B: No, don't give up! Have you heard of Anthony Webb?

3. A: No, I haven't. Who is he?

4. B: He was a basketball player. He was short, but he won the 1986 Slam Dunk Contest.

**Culture & Life**

1. The women's field hockey team from Zimbabwe surprised the whole world.

2. Although they had only a month to prepare, they won the gold medal at the 1980 Olympic Games.

**Let's Write**

1. My favorite sport is basketball.

2. However, I wasn't really good at it at first.

3. I couldn't shoot well unlike other players.

4. Although I felt discouraged, I didn't give up.

5. I practiced shooting for an hour every day.

6. This made me shoot well. Now, I'm the best player on our team.

# MEMO

# 적중100

영어 기출 문제집

## 정답 및 해설

지학 | 민찬규